Cissy® Identification & Price Guide

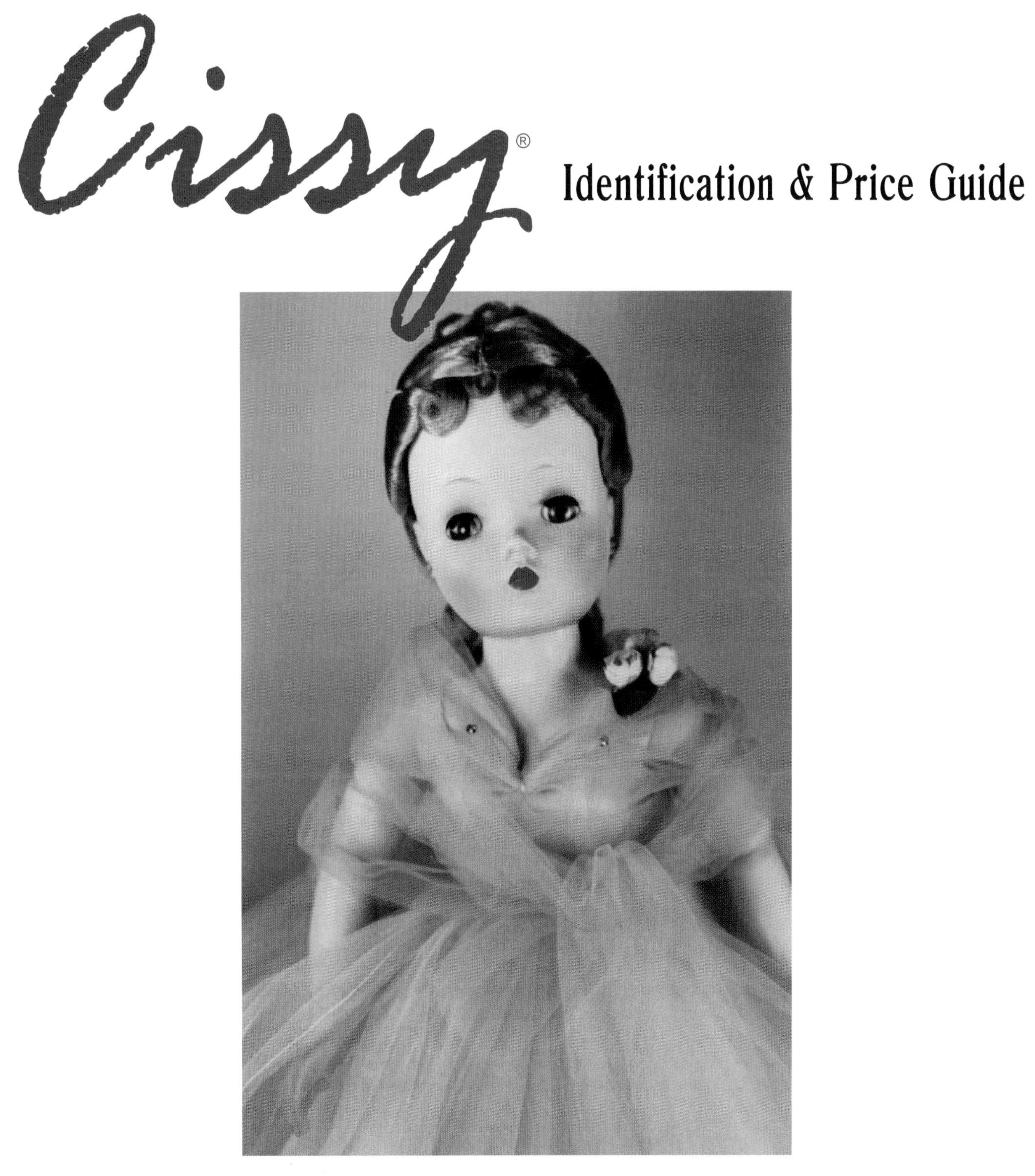

by A. Glenn Mandeville & Benita Cohen Schwartz

Published by

Hobby House Press, Inc.
Grantsville, Maryland
www.hobbyhouse.com

Cissy Identification & Price Guide is an independent study by the authors, A. Glenn Mandeville and Benita Cohen Schwartz and published by Hobby House Press, Inc. The manufacturer of the collectibles featured in this study did not sponsor the research and publication of this book in any way.

The values given within this book are intended as a value guide rather than arbitrarily set prices. The values quoted are as accurate as possible but in the case of errors, typographical, clerical or otherwise, the authors and publisher assume neither liability nor responsibility for any loss incurred by users of this book.

Photographs of the collectibles featured in this book were from the private collections of A. Glenn Mandeville or Benita Cohen Schwartz unless otherwise noted.

Additional copies of this book may be purchased at $29.95 (plus postage and handling) from
Hobby House Press, Inc.
1 Corporate Drive, Grantsville, MD 21536
1-800-554-1447
www.hobbyhouse.com
or from your favorite bookstore or dealer.

Printed in the United States of America

ISBN: 0-87588-626-4

Table of Contents

Dedication

This book is dedicated to Madame Alexander and her forward thinking ways that an adult fashion doll would set the trend for over half a century and is still going strong. Rarely does an artistic talent and a sense of business combine to create one of the geniuses of the 20th century. From humble beginnings to a glorious place in history, Madame Alexander was at the forefront of taking risks, making statements and keeping her business intact. She is a timeless role model that could succeed again even in these troubled times, for true talent knows no boundaries, no limits and cannot just sit back but move forward. Thank you Madame Alexander for all that you have left us.

Acknowledgements

Many thanks to Laura Colpus, Cynthia DiCaro, Ann Rast, and Helen Thomas who graciously provided photographs for this book. Your willingness to share your collections is much appreciated. Also thanks to Richard M. Chapman for historical research.

Opposite page: Cissy is wearing a dress typical of late 1950s women's fashion. *From the collection of Laura Colpus.*

Chapter 1

Cissy, The First Contemporary Fashion Doll

The year was 1955 and while many Americans were watching Lucy, another group of Americans are watching and reading all about the glamorous stars of the day and longed for that wonderful moment when they too, could be grown up and gorgeous. That group was the Baby Boomer children, the youngest approximately nine years old and ready to move onward and upward in a peace time economy.

Life was good...very good for most of mainstream America in the mid-1950s. The returning GI's from World War II were most anxious to settle into their tract house with white picket fence, a barbecue in the backyard and a wife that was a cross between Loretta Young and a housekeeper. Children were almost revered as now they could literally be raised in peace. Not since the previous century had there been a better decade in which to raise children.

New technology was creating another phenomenon, that of spare time. Miracle fibers that needed no ironing and appliances that made short work of boring chores meant that the entire family often had time for hobbies and even dreams.

The advances in both the motion picture industry and the new medium of the day, television, allowed all but the most rural families to compare themselves to the idealized families of the period. The Stones, the Nelsons, and the Burns families usually had a teenager or two. The movies of the times were catapulting new talent such as James Dean and Natalie Wood into celebrities to the preteen crowd.

The interesting thing was that many of the icons to the pre-teenagers WERE teenagers, and suddenly a young girl knew that if she followed a few simple lessons in grooming and manners that she could stand a chance of becoming pretty, pony tailed, perky and popular!

The doll industry was also in a state of transition. Little girls were learning that there might be more to life than a diaper pail. Careers never thought possible for women were opening up and the dreams of the American

This faux fur coat set was available as an extra boxed fashion in the 1950s. *From the collection of Laura Colpus.*

A very modern Cissy bride made in 1997.

teenager were not necessarily that of their mother. In fact, sometimes mother was not the best source for information on the new look and social morés because having been raised during the Great Depression and World War II, glamour often took a back seat to survival. Many times, the hero of the house was now a "big sister" with whom a preteen girl could glean volumes of information about what life in the teenage years could be like.

The Alexander Doll Company had for years featured glamorous large scale adult dolls, but the fact was that most were in period costumes and used cotton batting to create a bust line in the dress and had a standard toddler head mold and a leg mold with flat feet. A contemporary fashion doll, one that would serve as an inspiration to a little girl might be a next step.

One could always be sure that Madame Alexander had her finger on the pulse of what upper class America wanted. Her carriage trade approach to dolls had made her a legend.

In a daring move, at Toy Fair 1955, Madame Alexander unveiled Cissy, and billed her as "A Child's Dream Come True". The catalog states, "Every little girl dreams of being grown up. There is no one who hasn't seen a child walking around in mother's high heels. A bra too, and a dress or negligee can turn a humdrum day into a wonderful land of make-believe for a child. Now she can have all these unbelievable things in a doll to play with. Cissy, the doll with the figure and features of a debutante, is the newest and most exciting doll in the world. Her long slim body, her delicately molded bosom, her beautifully shaped feet that wear only high heeled shoes made just for her and her elegant costumes designed for her alone, make Cissy the shining wonder of the doll world. And she can walk too! One size—20 inches."

That introduction said it all, and the Alexander showroom on Fifth Avenue in New York City was a buzz with comments about the new doll that had an actual molded bosom and permanently arched high heel feet, for even Cissy's bedroom slippers would be high-heeled works of sophistication.

Perhaps the real issue was that Cissy was designed to teach a child how to be sophisticated. The wardrobe included real lingerie including bras and girdles, and movie star nightgowns and peignoirs. Obviously Cissy was not going to be hanging out the wash in a wrap around cotton housedress. Her cocktail dresses implied afternoons spent at the fashionable places and even her day dresses would be works of art. In short, Cissy was the glamorous fashion model type in doll form, a miniature combination of the top models of the day such as Suzy Parker, and the girl the child might long to become. Through interaction with Cissy and her wardrobe, the child could learn just

Opposite page: This African-American Cissy is part of the American Design Series produced in 1999. The ensemble was created by fashion designer Mark Bouwer.

how to mix and match all the astonishingly beautiful accessories that made a young debutante so popular.

In the days when the media was still the press, Toy Fair received a fair amount of coverage, mostly within the trade. Suffice it to say that some buyers and reporters were aghast at this new toy. Some felt that Madame Alexander, always known for impeccable good taste, had gone way too far. The doll was too sophisticated said some, and strayed from the homespun image of a child playing in the present with a likeness of herself. The future represented by Cissy in the opinion of some was one of a woman of perhaps questionable standards. Also her story line, although implied, was that Cissy was single and self-reliant without the need of a man to look after her.

Anecdotes say that Madame took on the press and the buyers and pointed out that the doll was merely a character like all her other dolls, and this time that character was no different than the models and movie stars that many adults themselves looked up to and emulated. Plus, the doll used the head mold of a child doll Madame had used for years. All this was much ado about nothing, stated a defiant Madame and within days the reports had changed touting Cissy as a breath of fresh air and a true thing of beauty. Madame had won and Cissy became the most popular doll of 1955 with toy buyers that had Alexander accounts.

By the end of 1955, the better stores were carrying extra ensembles for Cissy and even clothes racks and hat forms. The garments were so well constructed that if enlarged, would rival the real life fashions of the upper classes. Prices weren't cheap, but then neither would have been the adult size comparable item. Fashion accessories such as furs, rhinestone jewelry, pin on watches, corsage boxes, and separate millinery and lingerie were making Cissy into a real life doll debutante. The only thing lacking was hair play, for the doll came in two basic hairstyles, a short flip with bangs or a fancy hairdo with the sides pulled up, bangs and curled ends tied back. Some of the fancy ball gown dolls had unique hairstyles, but overall, those two basic styles adorned the head of the world's most glamorous doll.

Other toy companies soon realized that a high heel, full-figured, elegantly clothed doll was here to stay and thus began a fashion doll race in which nearly every toy company from large to small by 1957, had a fashion doll similar to Cissy in their line. Many, like the Revlon™ doll by Ideal™ used hair play to make up for the pricey gowns sported by Cissy. Others competed solely on eye appeal with garish long gowns that looked good only from the front. Some companies that sold dolls in such diverse places as hardware stores and grocery outlets had fashion dolls that weren't that bad...if you didn't have Cissy with which to compare them.

One can say that Cissy started it all and that statement would be correct. The doll was truly a work of art and if her purpose was to help little girls enter the world of sophistication, she would certainly have succeeded.

As the 1950s wore on, play patterns definitely changed. While the traditional bride and baby dolls would always remain a staple in any line, more and more children were interested in playing in the future. Role-playing was becoming popular as the Baby Boomer children drew nearer and nearer to the kingdom of teendom!

It is interesting to note that Cissy herself evolved as real life fashions put the emphasis on full skirts with crinolines and tight-fitting torso gowns with layers of tulle at the bottom. The doll was of course a mirror of what upper class women were wearing and it is interesting to trace the history of this genre of fashion by looking at the Alexander Doll Company catalogs over the mid to late 1950s.

By the early 1960s, the introduction of Sandra Dee and other young and fresh teenage stars such as Shelley Fabares and Elinor Donahue was changing the way American teenagers saw themselves. A new culture was developing in the late 1950s and on into the early 1960s as many young girls choose blue jeans, saddle shoes and one of daddy's old white shirts as the costume du jour!

Also, the scale of dolls had changed by 1958, and when Mattel™ introduced the Barbie® doll in 1959, the larger size dolls quickly faded from popularity in favor of the 11½" size doll.

During her heyday in the mid to late 1950s, Cissy set the trends not only in fashion, but also in influencing play patterns that to this day have not changed. Today, Cissy is back and as per the first time, she is still the most expensive and one of the most desirable of the sophisticated adult fashion dolls. This time the audience is squarely directed at adults, many who are meeting her for the very first time and it is love at first sight!

Cissy has an important place in our history of the American fashion doll, for she was the first in many ways and will always be yet another jewel in the crown of designer Madame Alexander. More than just a doll, Cissy represented a lifestyle of glamour and sophistication and offers us a three-dimensional view into a world often seen only in movies and fashion magazines.

Dare to dream again with Cissy and make her a part of your fashion doll collection today!

Madame Alexander
STYLE
2100
COLOR
HAIR
EYES
ALEXANDER DOLL COMPANY, NEW YORK N.Y.

Chapter 2

Cissy, A Legend Then...and Now!

Today's collector of vintage Cissy dolls is faced with the daunting fact that really mint or mint in box examples of even a more common street dressed doll can command upwards of over a thousand dollars. While always a pricey doll, vintage examples of the Cissy dolls and fashions are rising in price at a staggering rate. So what can one do?

Books on restoring vintage dolls have never been better and often a doll that has been gently played with and has an unlaundered costume can be had at a reasonable price. Because Cissy began in 1955, not many are found at garage or estate sales, as these dolls would have been sold for the most part long ago. One has to remember that half a century has gone by. Once in awhile, doll dealers at shows have Cissy dolls far below current prices and lucky finds from co-workers and other sources still happen. But with a little basic skill, a Cissy doll can be restored to near mint condition.

Another way to collect Cissy is to concentrate on the outstanding new editions of Cissy that are produced by the Alexander Doll Company. In 1996, Cissy made a grand comeback and like a true star, is still at the top of the fashion doll parade in terms of price structure, size and low edition size numbers. It is best to get on the best customer list with your favorite Alexander doll dealer as often times the dolls are sold out both at wholesale and the retail level before many collectors even learn about them!

Luckily for the Cissy collector, there really isn't that much difference between the vintage doll and the new incarnations of Cissy! The vintage doll has a hard plastic body, unmarked with two-piece vinyl arms and hard plastic legs that have a joint at the knee and a permanently arched high heel foot. The head is hard plastic, unmarked with sleep eyes and a glued on wig. Eye color is usually a shade of blue and it is unknown if variations are due to age or actual differences in eye color. Hair styles were usually one of two—a short flip with short bangs or longer, flat bangs, sides pulled up and a long, one length piece from the crown down to the nape of the neck ending in curls and tied with a ribbon or an elastic. A metal bar held the sides up across the top

Opposite page: A basic Cissy from the 1950s wearing her lace chemise and elastic strap shoes.

of the head and each side piece was tied with string. The hair is very sparse on Cissy and it is evident that the hairstyle was not meant to be disturbed. Colors vary from a dark brown, to an ash blonde. Red heads and brunettes seem to be slightly harder to find than the "Tosca" (the company name for ash blonde.)

One of the most troublesome situations with a vintage Cissy is missing eyelashes. Many times however, the glue that held the eyelashes in place has deteriorated and with a pair of tweezers, the eyelashes can be gently pulled forward and out, and with a bit of fabric glue, repositioned in the slot for them. One might choose to have a professional do this although it is an easy repair. Examine a doll carefully with missing eyelashes to determine if they are just pushed back or have actually been lost.

The contemporary Cissy doll of today is much like her older sister. The major differences are that the arms are one piece, like the last years of Cissy circa 1961-1962. The head mold is basically the same, marked but in vinyl. The glued on wigs are varied and many, and unlike the vintage dolls, can be restyled or even replaced with clever designs from various sources. Because the doll's head is vinyl, re-rooting the head with new hair is often possible. The eyes still open and close and have the same look to them as the vintage dolls, but come in all colors: blue, green, brown and even violet.

Cissy was not designed to be a hard play doll, but a display doll for her varied and many fashions and accessories. This is true today with both vintage and contemporary dolls.

The collector of the current Cissy dolls has many, many choices and ways to make Cissy a part of their fashion doll collection. Perhaps the best collections might have an example of a vintage doll with a current offering. One thing is for sure...Cissy is a doll worth collecting and displaying be it vintage or contemporary!

Cissy's Measurements

	Vintage	Modern
Height	20-21″	21″
Bust	9″	8½″
Waist	6½″	6″
Hips	8″	7½″
Neck-Crotch	7¾″	7¾″
Foot Length	2¼″	2¼″

Opposite page: Ebony and Ivory Houndstooth Suit is a vinyl head Cissy from 1996. Her dog is by Annalee Doll Company.

Chapter 3

The Faces of Cissy

It's all about faces. Each decade has THE face that defines the period. Sometimes several looks created "THE LOOK" of the decade.

While Cissy was made from the same mold, it is easy to see the changes over the years. One who thinks that hairstyles and make-up matter little should think again. The same blank face is like a canvas that can forever be painted upon and Cissy has proven that. The collector today is most fortunate as Cissy in all her ethnic guises proves once again that a thing of beauty is indeed a joy forever.

The vintage Cissy dolls mirrored the haute couture and very precise make-up of the 1950s.

In the early 1990s, Cissy's brush with pseudo-fame tried to recapture a look of the vintage dolls with some degree of success but that time period had it's own look and these dolls fell a bit short.

The Caucasian Cissy of today is a nostalgic blend of retro looks and up to the minute make-up. Depending upon the ensemble, Cissy's face reflects exactly what the designer is trying to communicate. The vinyl head lends itself beautifully to new eye colors and hairstyles.

African-American Cissy joined the Alexander Doll Company line-up in 1996. Breathtaking in many ways, these dolls were eagerly accepted by collectors of all races. She is wonderful and a great addition to any collection.

Many doll companies are experimenting with a mixture of skin tones, eye coloring and make-up. The Collector's United Fortune Teller is just such a doll. It shows the many possibilities of Cissy.

Chapter 4

The 1950s—A Child's Dreams Come True

For America, 1955 was a major year in history. Changes were everywhere for the Baby Boomer children and the post World War II generation. One word captured the dreams of children and that word was Disney. Walt Disney opened his dream theme park, Disneyland, carved out of an orange grove in California. "Disneymania" took over as both boys and girls became enchanted with being on center stage. On television, *The Mickey Mouse Club* debuted and made ordinary children into household celebrities overnight. The television show had enough for every child to enjoy from Fess Parker as Davy Crockett to Annette Funicello dancing her way in mouse ears. In many ways, 1955 was perhaps a stellar year.

A vaccine developed by Dr. Jonas Salk finally conquered poliomyelitis or infantile paralysis, the last of the childhood plagues that was feared by parents and children. It seemed as if there was a lot for which to be thankful!

America was alive with new concepts. McDonald's fast food started their first franchise, Ann Landers debuted in the *Chicago Sun-Tim*es, the youth of America discovered rock 'n roll with *Rock Around the Clock* by Bill Haley and the Comets, which remained at number one for eight straight weeks. Kenner Toys also introduced Play-Doh.

Rebel Without a Cause turned James Dean into a star in 1955, but it was short lived as he was tragically killed four days after the release of the movie. The word "teenager" took on new significance in the lives of children and young adults and perhaps changed play patterns forever.

Yes, a child's dream would come true as stated in the Alexander Doll Company catalogs. The timing was right for children to play in the future and what better doll offered that chance than Cissy, every little girl's dream of being grown up.

The debut of Cissy was perfect timing. The doll was based on the child's need to play in the future—in a world of grown-up fantasy where a negligee

Opposite page: This dotted nylon net gown has a pink taffeta underskirt and a giant horsehair flowered trimmed hat. #2160, 1957. *From the collection of Helen Thomas.*

can turn a ho-hum day into make believe, as was stated in the Alexander company catalogs. Things would never be the same!

For 1956, the Alexander Doll Company catalog showed proof that Cissy was a success. The typical staircase photograph in the catalog, entitled "Cissy Fashion Parade," featured even more luxurious formals and accessories. The dressed dolls were full skirted and of course the day dresses featured hats, most with veils and flower trim.

The catalog stated, "Cissy, our wonderful grown-up doll was made with great understanding of the mind and heart of a child-still young, but longing to be grown-up, a combination of reality and make-believe. Cissy, the doll with the figure and features of a debutante is the most popular doll in the world."

And what a world 1956 was! Elvis Presley had four chart topping songs by the end of the year and he was also a television sensation and guest of the formerly rather conservative *Ed Sullivan Show*. Sullivan later said that Elvis was one of the most well-mannered guests ever to appear on his show! The world was changing into one of teen idols and youngsters who looked up to them. It was not such a reach for an eight-year-old to dream of being a teenager. The movie stars and television idols were less than a decade away for many children, a phenomenon that appeared to propel the change in play patterns from one of playing in the present to one of projecting oneself into the glamorous and sophisticated world that lay just ahead!

Glamour seemed to be everywhere and not just on Cissy. Brigitte Bardot at twenty-two years old became legendary with her film *And God Created Woman*, and on Broadway, *My Fair Lady* debuted starring Julie Andrews. It ran for 2,717 performances, a total of six years! Perhaps the most like Cissy was actress and beauty Grace Kelly, who at 26, married Prince Rainier in what many would call the fairy tale wedding of the century in 1956. Americans dreamed of more and the dolls and toys showed an ever-increasing obsession with quality and detail.

Cissy, at 21 inches tall, was considered by many to be THE doll of the decade in a previously unimagined size and shape. As children dreamed of a not-too-distant-future, the music of the times changed with varied artists such as Dean Martin, Gogi Grant and Elvis Presley representing differing styles of music.

One can say that 1956 established itself as the year that fashion dreams came true as well, as more and more easy care fibers were incorporated into glamorous fashions that not only Cissy, but real life women wore everyday.

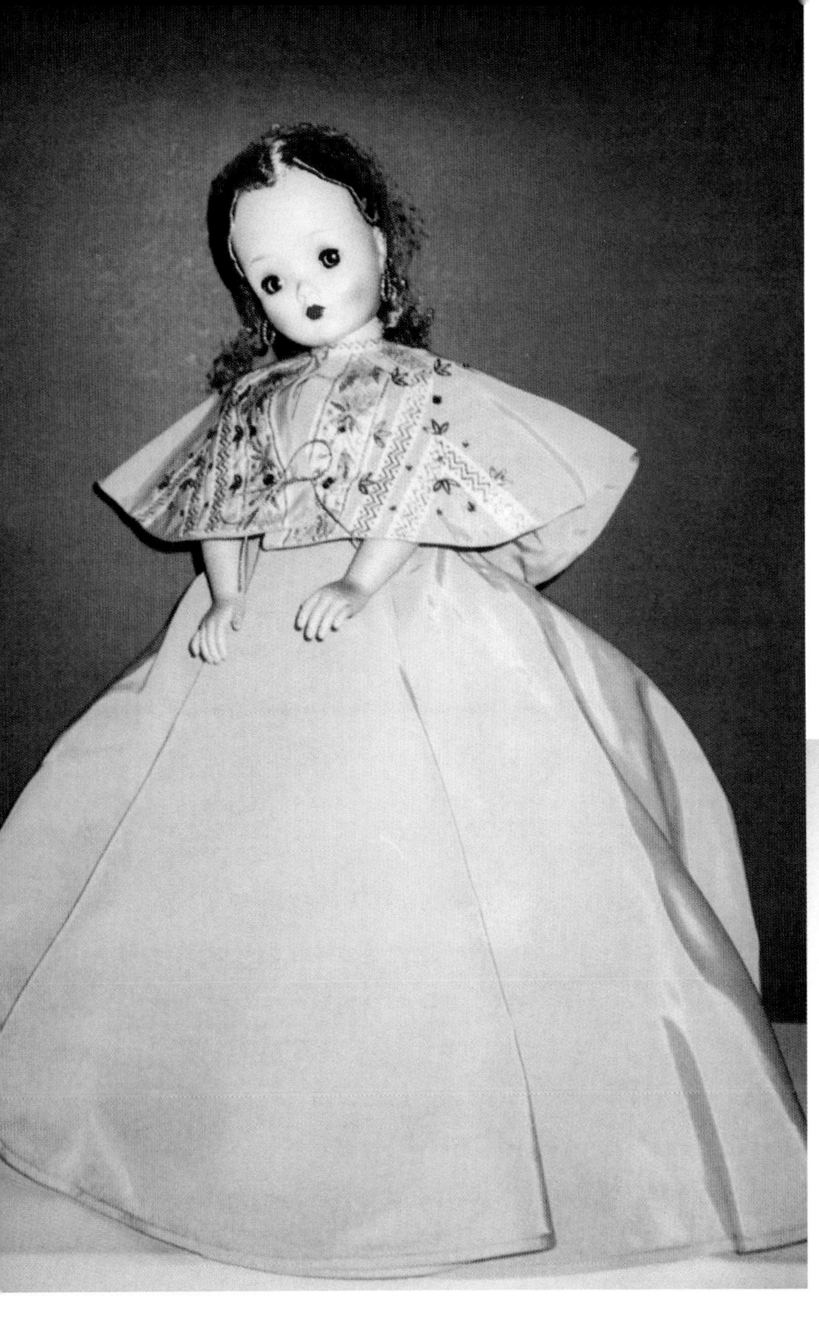

#2098, 1955 - A gold taffeta evening gown with a matching cape trimmed with gold braid. *From the collection of Laura Colpus.*

#2173 was made in 1957 and is a black velvet princess cut gown with an orlon fur stole. Notice the fingerless gloves. *From the collection of Helen Thomas.*

The look of sophistication became easier for the average woman to attain, and for young children playing with Cissy, it was easy to be excited about that future!

The Alexander Doll Company's 1957 Cissy collection was titled "Cissy Models Her Formal Gowns" and the catalog proclaimed, "Cissy, our wonderful grown-up doll started a whole new trend in doll manufacturing. She makes it possible for the little girl to play make-believe in the most wonderful way, with a doll having the figure and features of a debutante and a doll wearing the smart sophisticated clothes of a young lady."

It was obvious that there were three elements that were selling with Cissy—the formal gowns, the now taffeta afternoon and cocktail dresses, and the boxed fashions and accessories. All the stops were pulled out and the boxed fashions allowed even more play value for Cissy. One could even purchase a clothes rack and a hat stand for Cissy. Perhaps the child was almost overwhelmed by the 1957 line. (Certainly the parent was in many cases, as glamour at the top doesn't come cheap!) Tiny gloves, sunglasses, "mink" stoles, hankies and hats along with jewelry, were all just a part of a day in the life of Cissy. Fantasy play abounded that year, as Cissy was available as a bride and even as Lady Hamilton!

The first waves of the Baby Boomers still played with dolls, but got closer and closer to crossing over into being teenagers.

American pop culture reflected the angst of young love as teenage movie and television stars made fantasy into reality. Tab Hunter sang about young love and Buddy Knox loved his party dolls. Debbie Reynolds sang of love while Pat Boone told of love letters in the sand. This trend continued at the box office with one of the hottest films of the year, *Tammy and the Bachelor* with Debbie Reynolds and Leslie Nielsen.

It was amazing that America had come so far since the end of World War II. Children became a luxury item rather than a necessity to tend to the fields and care for the home. The suburbs filled with tract houses surrounded by white picket fences—the norm for many. The play patterns of children were firmly entrenched in the future by now. While baby dolls that needed to be cared for were never out of style, the dominating force of the doll world was definitely the high heeled, full-figured fashion doll that debuted with Cissy and continued as more mainstream and smaller manufacturers offered the same with varying degrees of quality.

Above: #2100, 1955 - A long torso gown of mauve taffeta with a large multi-taffeta bow. *From the collection of Helen Thomas.*

Left: Another torso gown from 1955, notice the variation of the taffeta bow. *From the collection of Helen Thomas.*

Yet while all this self-absorption went on, America received a jolt that Russia, considered technologically inferior by many scientists, had won the race to space as the Soviet Union launched the world's first artificial satellite, Sputnik I in November of 1957. Still, the American teenager and the children waiting to be just that, danced on the now #1 dance party show, *American Bandstand*, with host Dick Clark which went national in 1957 on the ABC television network. For the younger child, perhaps those playing with Cissy, Theodore Seuss Geisel under the pen name Dr. Seuss published his book, *The Cat in the Hat*. It was an interesting year.

Fashion never stays static for very long and Cissy was no exception. While the 1958 catalog no longer felt the need to extol the virtues of the 21 inch "most popular doll in the world," it was obvious that Cissy was still the star in the crown at the Alexander Doll Company. The catalog merely stated the facts...that Cissy was here and the prettiest girl in town and her gown collection was titled "Dolls to Remember."

Back again was yet another bride doll, which showed that for many young girls, that fantasy was alive and well. For the more adventuresome, Cissy as The Lady in Red was a vision in flocked red dots on tulle with a taffeta underskirt. Cissy was also shown as a Queen reminiscent of the Coronation of Queen Elizabeth in England, one of Madame Alexander's favorite topics.

The dolls had a richer, creamier look to the hard plastic. Examples have been found with cheek blush applied first, then the entire head airbrushed in a flesh tone so that the blush shone through rather than applied on top. Other dolls from this year still had the paler face from the 1955-56 line. The doll was merely a mannequin to Madame Alexander, a fact that can't be stated enough. Her dreams were draped on Cissy for what she thought the sophisticated young lady of the day should be!

The regular line of Cissy dolls reflected the new closer to the body silhouette often modeled by Suzy Parker, one of the top models of the day. The look for daytime was a big hat, with a veil of course and a sheath dress often with a matching coat that fell below the knees. White gloves of course were required. In fact, Cissy sold so well that Madame Alexander actually advertised the doll less often, a good sign that the public already knew the power of the name. Still, the Alexander Doll Company was amazingly naive in our opinion, in some ways, to ignore the threat posed by the 10½ inch fashion dolls such as Little Miss Revlon®, Jill®, Miss Ginger® and Toni®. In

#2041, 1956 is a satin ball gown with an orlon fur stole. *From the collection of Helen Thomas.*

Below: A similar evening gown with a different neckline. *From the collection of Laura Colpus.*

Below: Another view. *From the collection of Helen Thomas.*

addition, the category of dolls in the same size as Cissy rapidly expanded with top toy companies such as Ideal™ and American Character™ showing strong lines with the Revlon® doll, Toni® and Sweet Sue Sophisticate®. America had embraced the fashion doll concept, and with each passing year, the genre was incorporated into pop culture and history.

The Jet Age arrived in 1958 when British Overseas Airways launched the first transatlantic passenger jet service. The flying time from New York City to London was cut in half. The term "Jet Setter" now applied to those able and willing to travel! Cissy would have been right at home in First Class! To make buying Cissy easier, 1958 was the year that the American Express card debuted.

While much too youthful for Cissy, the Hula Hoop was the ultimate late Baby Boomer toy. At the movies, Leslie Caron and Maurice Chevalier starred in *Gigi*, a movie that took home a staggering nine Academy Awards! Stereophonic sound became the password for movies and recordings. Music became more and more teen themed. Danny & and the Juniors were at the hop, it was about twilight time with The Platters, and the Everly Brothers said that all they had to do was dream.

Despite the push for teenage theme icons, television was into westerns, as *Gunsmoke* became the number one show of the year. Still, Cissy was at the top but change was just around the corner. The decade ended with a bang and not from one on the prairie!

Once again, Cissy was not the cover doll on the 1959 Alexander catalog. Spinning changes were happening. Miniature fashion dolls as well as companion or life-size toddler dolls, overtook the larger dolls of the day plus Mattel™ debuted the Barbie® doll which had clothing made in the grand tradition in Japan versus the United States at a fraction of the price. Tastes changed and with the introduction of the Barbie® doll, it was clear that children selected their own toys, a new concept for the time. Indeed, television brought a new influence into the home, and one that would, until this day, control the doll and toy industry.

Madame Alexander considered the choice of a toy to be up to the parent, and the company had never had to advertise their products in what was considered a vulgar new medium by many, television. Cissy was relegated to the better stores and parents or grandparents made the expensive decision to bring Cissy into the life of a child.

Commonly known as the Camellia Ball Gown, the velvet stole is also lined in the same camellia print fabric.

The doll was made in 1958 and is #2283.

Lovely goldenrod tulle gown accented with flowers is from the late 1950s. *From the collection of Helen Thomas.*

The world of 1959 was a different place. The running of an American household was the subject of the great kitchen debate when Vice-President Richard Nixon arrived in Moscow to open the American National Exposition, which was a rare showing of American culture. According to reports, Nikita Khrushchev was not in the mood for such a display. It was a rare time in history when two leaders spoke candidly about day-to-day life in two opposite countries.

At home in the USA, Cissy was shown as a glowing bride, and in a heavy slipper satin cocktail dress as many society women still lunched at The Plaza. Full skirts with crinolines and fitted tops still graced Cissy's fantastic torso, reflecting styles long since past in movies like *White Christmas* going back to 1955.

The times once again were changing. At the movie theater, more changes took place. Old Hollywood glamour competed with young love as Marilyn Monroe sizzled the screen with *Some Like it Hot*, while barely legal love was on the big screen with *Gidget*, which would be a major name and responsible for changes in the doll world for at least fifteen years. Television was ablaze with *Gunsmoke*, *Wagon Train*, and *Maverick* but yet down to earth with *The Real McCoys*. Game shows such as *I've Got a Secret,* which still played up the glamour of the celebrity panelists who entered the show in their flowing gowns clung to the elegant fashions of the time which the Cissy doll still exemplified.

The recording industry was in the same transition as The Platters, Frankie Avalon, Paul Anka and Bobby Darin all had Billboard #1 hits that year. Berry Gordy launched Motown, and girl groups from the Motor City soon overtook guy teen idols from south Philadelphia.

Meanwhile, the doll wars were just heating up as changes in scale, which had started in the late 1950s, continued. Cissy was still a strong selling doll for the carriage trade, but it was almost inevitable that a smaller scale doll eventually took over. Even Madame Alexander herself introduced Cissette, a 10½ inch version of Cissy in 1957. Once again, Madame was often the uncredited leader of a fashion doll trend.

One could say that the decade of the 1950s was one of unparalleled prosperity formerly unseen in this century and also spawned the birth of the teenager being as important of an influence in movies and television as the old Hollywood vanguard. The next decade brought even more change.

#2036 from 1956 was a shell pink taffeta gown with diagonal side drapery, shown here is a rose pink version. *From the collection of Helen Thomas.*

Below: And a red version of #2036, 1956. *From the collection of Helen Thomas.*

Below: A blue variation of #2025, 1956. The gown is ankle length, just perfect to dance the night away at the ball.

#2043, 1956 is a black velvet fitted torso gown with a flounce of black tulle. Her flared neckline is pink satin.

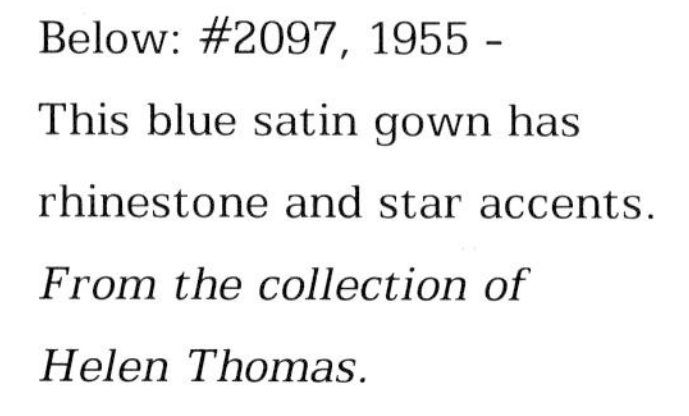

Below: #2097, 1955 - This blue satin gown has rhinestone and star accents. *From the collection of Helen Thomas.*

Below: Close up of the ostrich feather fan and a detail of the rhinestone and star accents. *From the collection of Helen Thomas.*

This yellow tulle ball gown is perfect for dancing and was produced in the late 1950s. Notice the sprinkling of rhinestones on the tulle

The same tulle ball gown in pale green. *From the collection of Laura Colpus.*

This purple velvet torso gown is lined with pink satin at the neck and has a lilac tulle flounce skirt accented with flowers, #2174, 1957. *From the collection of Helen Thomas.*

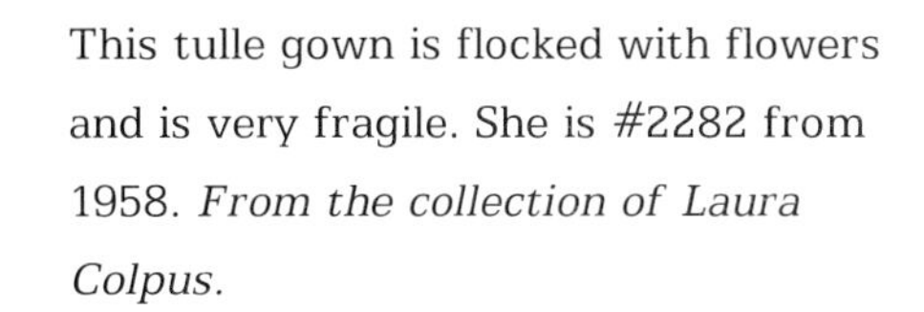

This tulle gown is flocked with flowers and is very fragile. She is #2282 from 1958. *From the collection of Laura Colpus.*

A close up showing the horsehair hat, and more detail of the floral flocking. *From the collection of Helen Thomas.*

This rare 1955 Cissy Bride is commonly called the 'Forever Darling' bride and is based on the bridal gown worn by Lucille Ball in the movie with the same name. She is not pictured in the company catalog. *From the collection of Helen Thomas.*

#2101, 1955 - A white brocade bridal gown with appliqués of pearls and rhinestones throughout the dress. Instead of a bouquet of flowers, she carries a tulle muff decorated with flowers. *From the collection of Helen Thomas.*

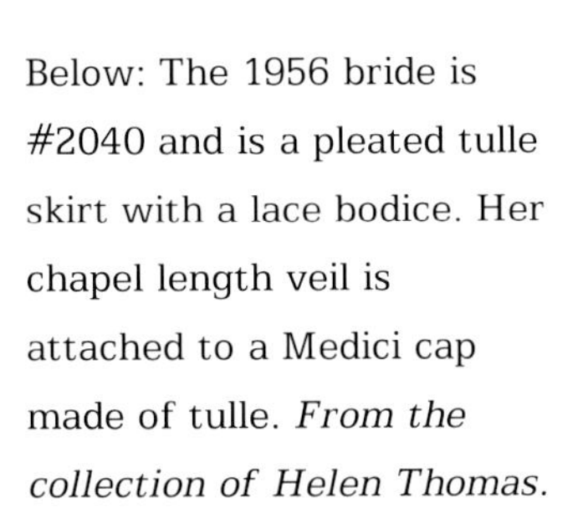

Below: The 1956 bride is #2040 and is a pleated tulle skirt with a lace bodice. Her chapel length veil is attached to a Medici cap made of tulle. *From the collection of Helen Thomas.*

Below: Close up of the 1956 bride. *From the collection of Helen Thomas.*

Right: #2030 is the Cissy Bridesmaid from 1956, similar in style to the bride with a blue tulle skirt and net bodice sparkling with silver threads. *From the collection of Ann Rast.*

Below: #2170, is the style number for the 1959 Bride. She is wearing a tulle gown with puffed sleeves, a lace bodice, and a full-length tulle veil. *From the collection of Helen Thomas.*

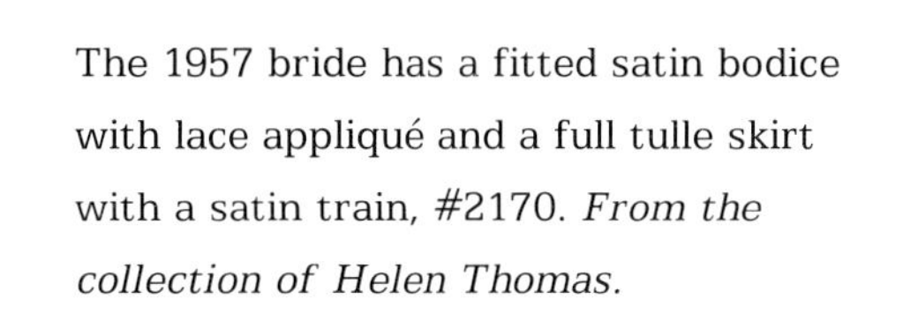

The 1957 bride has a fitted satin bodice with lace appliqué and a full tulle skirt with a satin train, #2170. *From the collection of Helen Thomas.*

A close-up view of the 1957 bride showing the detailing on her bodice. *From the collection of Helen Thomas.*

In 1958, Madame used the embroidered bridal wreath pattern on all the bride dolls produced that year. She has a full-length tulle veil. *From the collection of Helen Thomas.*

This white organdy gown is from the first group of Cissy dolls produced in 1955, #2095.

#2035, 1956 is an organdy garden party dress over a blue slip. Very southern belle. *From the collection of Helen Thomas.*

This Cissy Queen looks so regal in her white brocade gown reminiscent of Queen Elizabeth.

Gainsborough Cissy is #2176 from 1957 and is wearing a blue taffeta gown with a matching hat trimmed with pink flowers. *From the collection of Helen Thomas.*

Cocktail dress. *From the collection of Helen Thomas.*

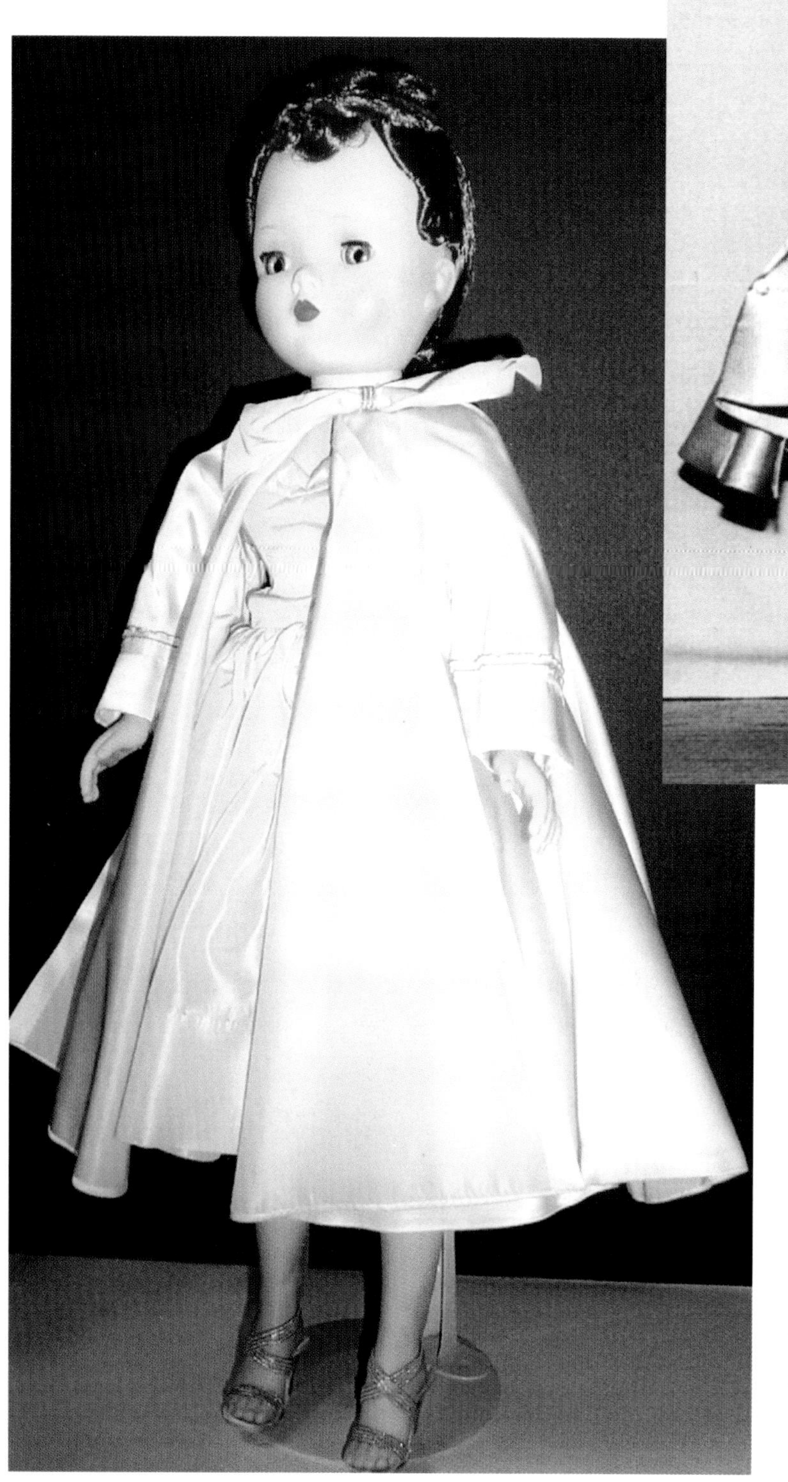

Left: #2021, 1956 is ready for the theater in this full-skirted aqua sleeveless taffeta dress and an ivory satin coat lined with the aqua taffeta. *From the collection of Laura Colpus.*

Similar to #2021, shown are 2 different color versions, champagne and gold. The dresses are the same color as the coat. *From the collection of Helen Thomas.*

#2012, 1956, a simple taffeta dress with a simple white tulle and straw hat, but it still makes a statement. *From the collection of Laura Colpus.*

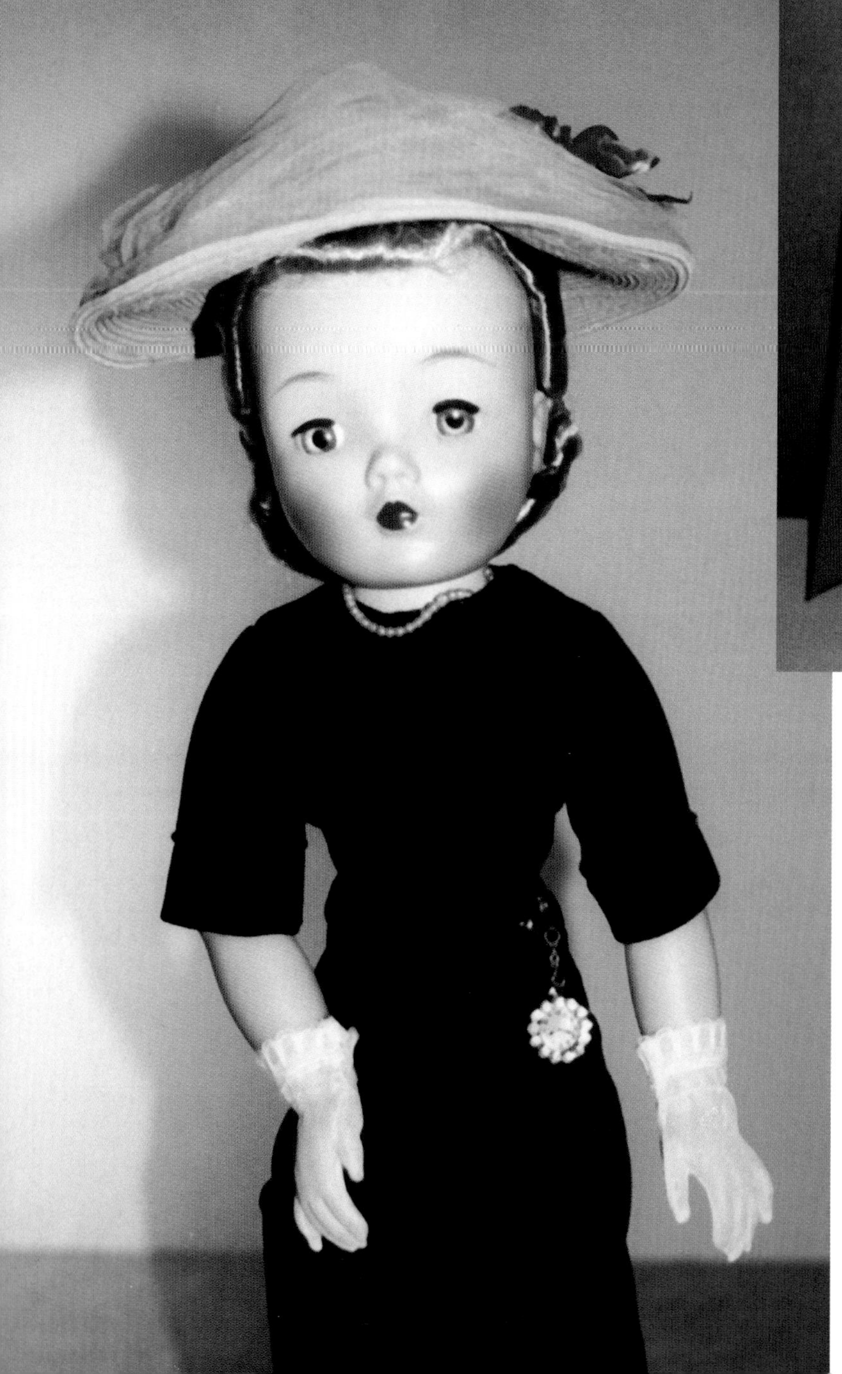

This black velvet sheath from 1958, gets a splash of color with her aqua hat. *From the collection of Helen Thomas.*

This beautiful blue brocade cocktail dress has a matching shawl. She even has matching blue gloves. *From the collection of Helen Thomas.*

Another version of the same dress only this time in ruby red. It was also produced in emerald green. *From the collection of Helen Thomas.*

This lavender taffeta dress has a matching bolero jacket with a straw hat and a clear handbag. She is #2143 from 1957. *From the collection of Ann Rast.*

Left: #2141, 1957 is a navy taffeta sleeveless dress with a white ruffled organdy cape and white sheer gloves. Notice the rhinestone watch dangling at the doll's waist. *From the collection of Helen Thomas.*

Opposite page: #2017, 1956. This aqua taffeta dress has a can-can petticoat under it. It's topped with a black velvet bolero. Perfect for cocktails.

Above: #2091, 1955 - This black taffeta cocktail ensemble comes complete with the clear plastic purse decorated with flowers. Her pink hat matches her pink taffeta and net petticoat. *From the collection of Laura Colpus.*

Left: A lovely satin cocktail ensemble from the 1950s. Simple lines with just the right little extras like the sheer lace cuffed gloves. *From the collection of Laura Colpus.*

A basic black dress accessorized with a fur stole, a bright red veiled hat, and pearls is the perfect ensemble for lunch at the country club.

This sapphire blue satin cocktail dress has a matching stole with a brooch closure. Notice the pearl handbag. She is #2120 from 1959. *From the collection of Helen Thomas.*

#2019 is a red dotted Swiss organdy dress over a white taffeta slip. *From the collection of Helen Thomas.*

Another dotted Swiss dress with interesting lace detailing on the cuffs. *From the collection of Helen Thomas.*

A sheer print dress accented with lace and topped with an interesting hat makes Cissy ready for an afternoon garden party. *From the collection of Ann Rast.*

Opposite page: #2084, 1955 - This navy taffeta dress has a matching bolero jacket. Notice the extra details on the hat - lace, tulle, and flowers.

This pink satin cocktail dress is #2252 from 1958 and has a tulle stole secured by a rose corsage. She carries a clear plastic handbag and has white sheer gloves. *From the collection of Helen Thomas.*

This golden yellow print dress comes with a wide brimmed black hat was produced in 1957 and is #2120.

#2014 1956, a simple cotton shirtwaist dress becomes something special when paired with a black velvet hat with a veil. *From the collection of Laura Colpus.*

A two-piece suit with rhinestone accents is perfect as a traveling suit for Cissy. *From the collection of Helen Thomas.*

One of Cissy's many cotton dresses with a dropped waist from the 1950s. *From the collection of Helen Thomas.*

Another cotton print dress. *From the collection of Laura Colpus.*

A third dropped waist dress, has also been found in pink. This is #2222 from 1958. *From the collection of Laura Colpus.*

This aqua polished cotton dress is #2130 from 1957. *From the collection of Helen Thomas.*

#2083, 1955 - Can't miss Cissy in this bright red cotton dress and striped blouse. Of course under her skirt is a white taffeta can-can slip. *From the collection of Cynthia DiCaro.*

This two-piece pink and white striped cotton skirt ensemble looks perfect on Cissy. *From the collection of Laura Colpus.*

But remove the skirt and there's a whole new look! *From the collection of Laura Colpus.*

Lavender print shirtwaist dress, #2232 with a purple flower-trimmed hat was produced in 1958. *From the collection of Laura Colpus.*

This polished cotton dress is so feminine with the wide lace collar. *From the collection of Laura Colpus.*

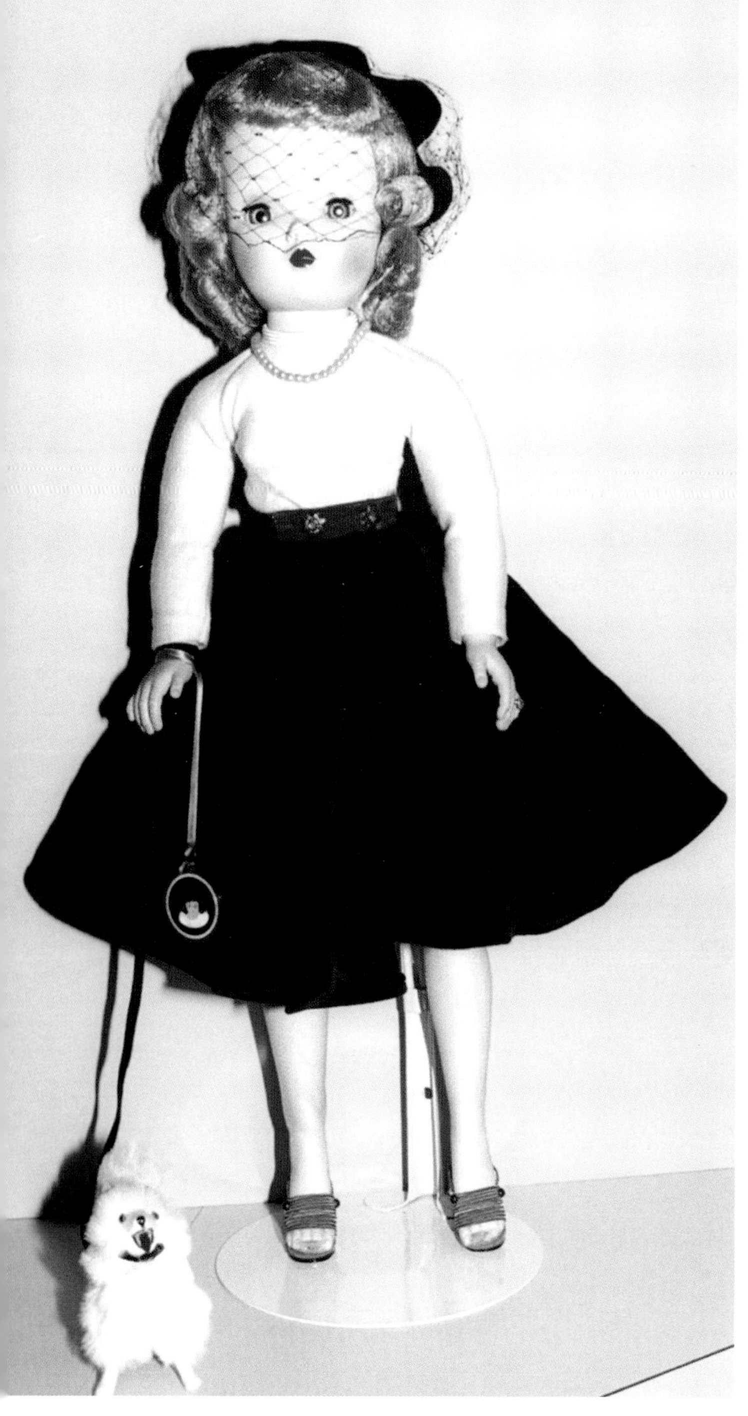

Cissy Walks her Dog is from 1956, another simple ensemble made interesting with the veiled hat and studded waistband. *From the collection of Helen Thomas.*

This lavender striped cotton blouse with matching solid skirt is circa 1957. *From the collection of Helen Thomas.*

#2115 from 1959 is a gold lace skirt topped with a bright blue jersey shirt and a gold belt. Notice the accent; the brooch and floral garland. *From the collection of Helen Thomas.*

Lovely full shirtwaist polka dot dress topped with a white straw hat tied with a big tulle bow, circa 1958. *From the collection of Helen Thomas.*

One of the hundreds of extra ensembles sold separately for Cissy was this polished cotton polka dot sundress. Notice the little details added—the buttons on the bodice and the bows on the shoulders.

The sundress shown in its original box.

Circa late 1950s is this black shirt with a blue print circle skirt with lots of crinoline. *From the collection of Laura Colpus.*

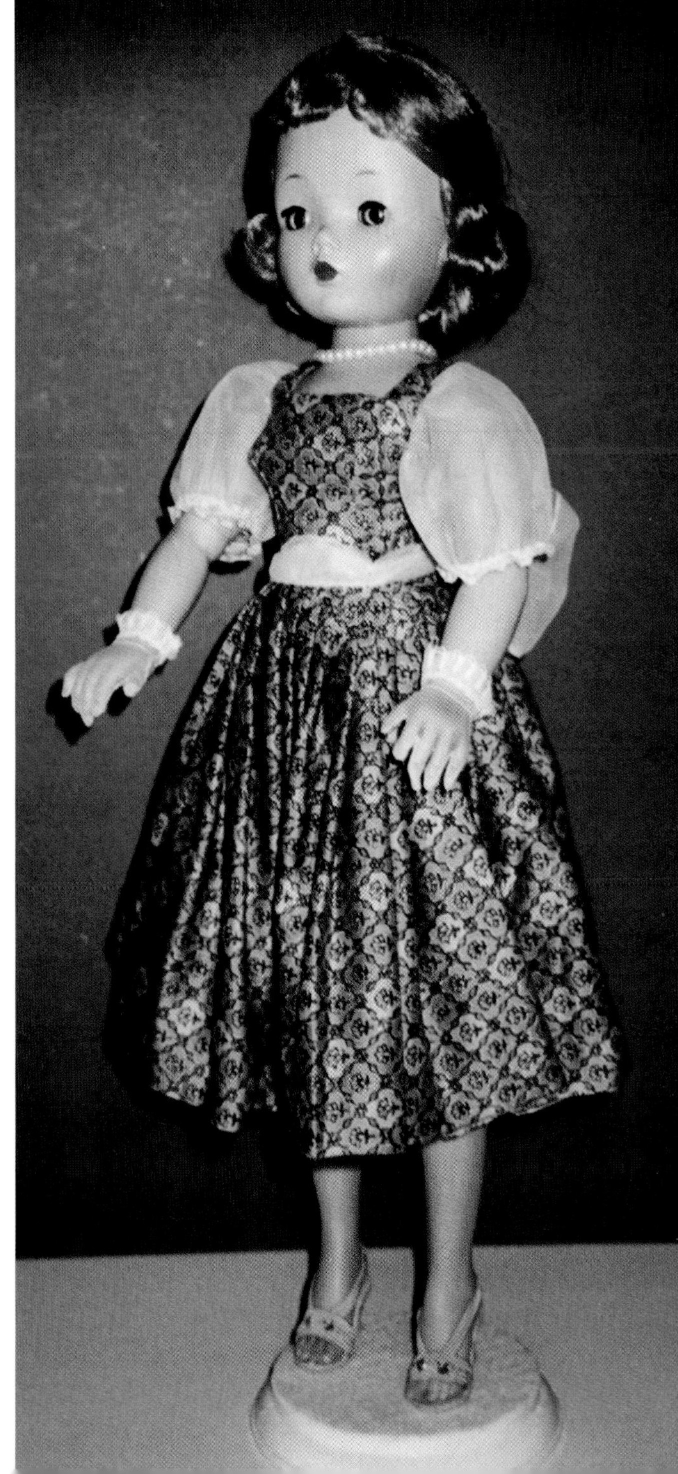

A print polished cotton dress accented with organdy puffed sleeves and sash make this boxed fashion more than just another cotton dress. *From the collection of Laura Colpus.*

This cotton dress with organdy sleeves is done in a harder-to-find cotton floral print. *From the collection of Laura Colpus.*

While there were many complete fashions sold separately, there were also mix and match separates. Some were sold as individual pieces and others were sold in groups. *From the collection of Laura Colpus.*

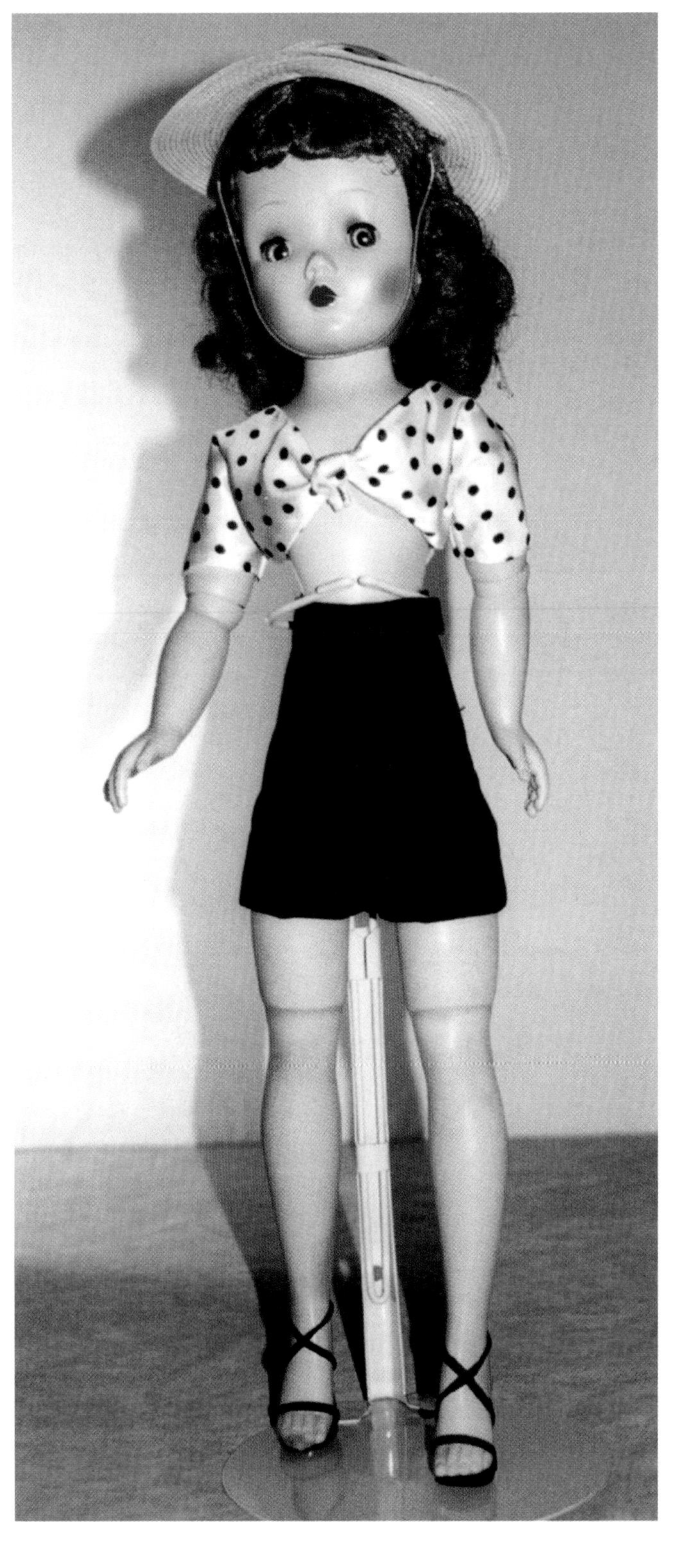

Another great example of mix and match separates. A skirt paired with a long jacket is great for a walk on the boardwalk. Underneath is a cute beach outfit of shorts and a midriff top. *From the collection of Helen Thomas.*

A boxed cabana ensemble consisting of a polished cotton bathing suit with a matching overskirt. Cissy models the cabana outfit. *From the collection of Helen Thomas*

Another cabana outfit in yellow striped cotton. *From the collection of Laura Colpus.*

Below: A close up view of the bathing suit. *From the collection of Laura Colpus.*

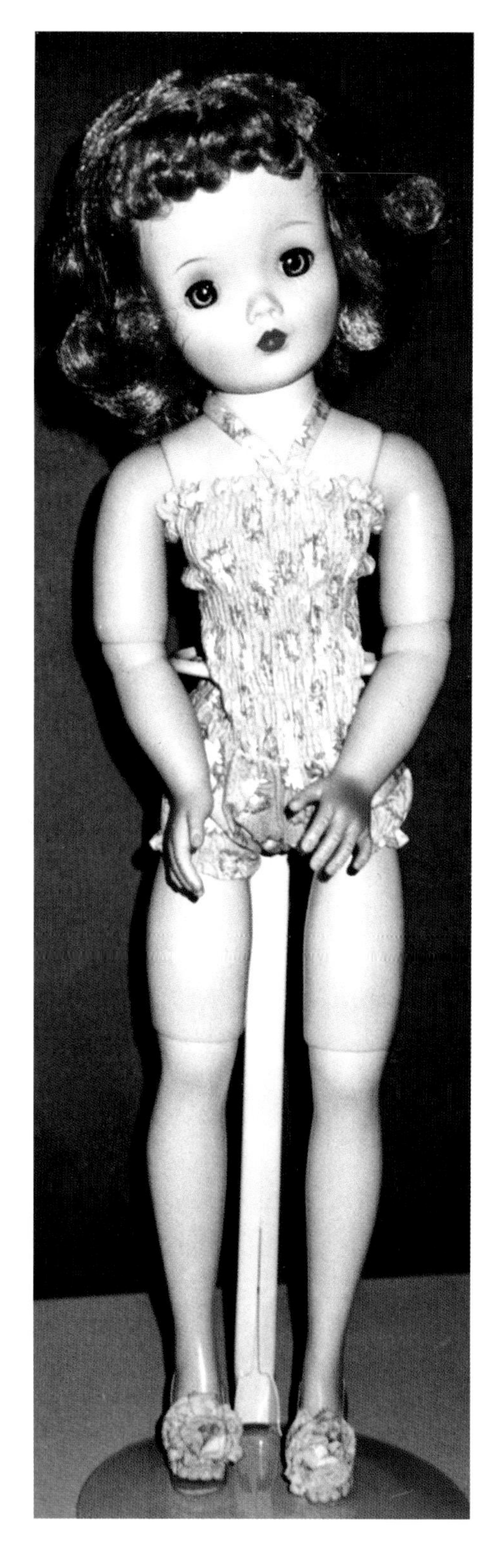

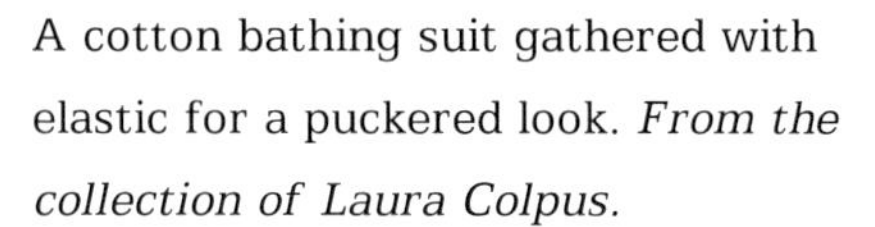

A cotton bathing suit gathered with elastic for a puckered look. *From the collection of Laura Colpus.*

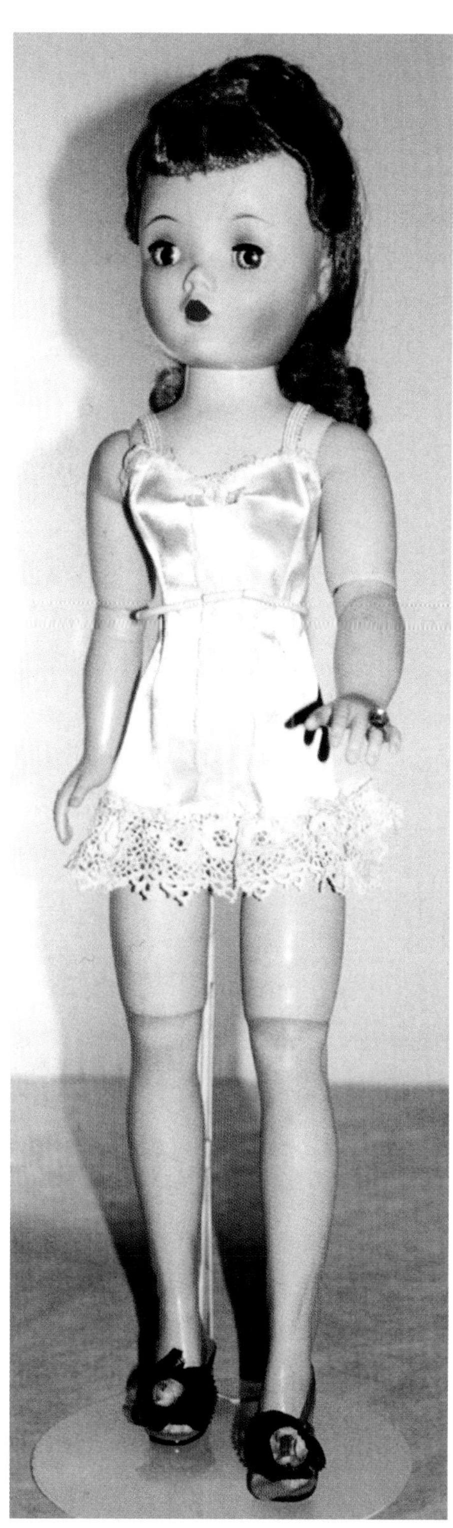

Right: A basic Cissy wearing a chemise trimmed with crocheted lace. *From the collection of Helen Thomas.*

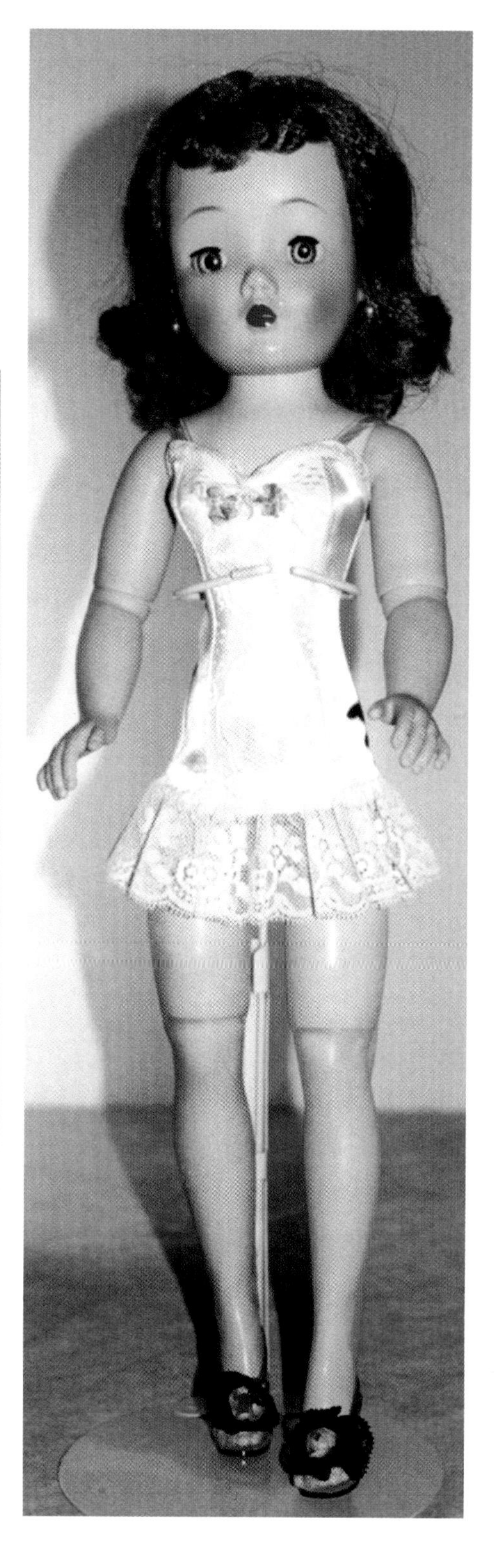

Another chemise for Cissy. She also had black lace lingerie. *From the collection of Helen Thomas.*

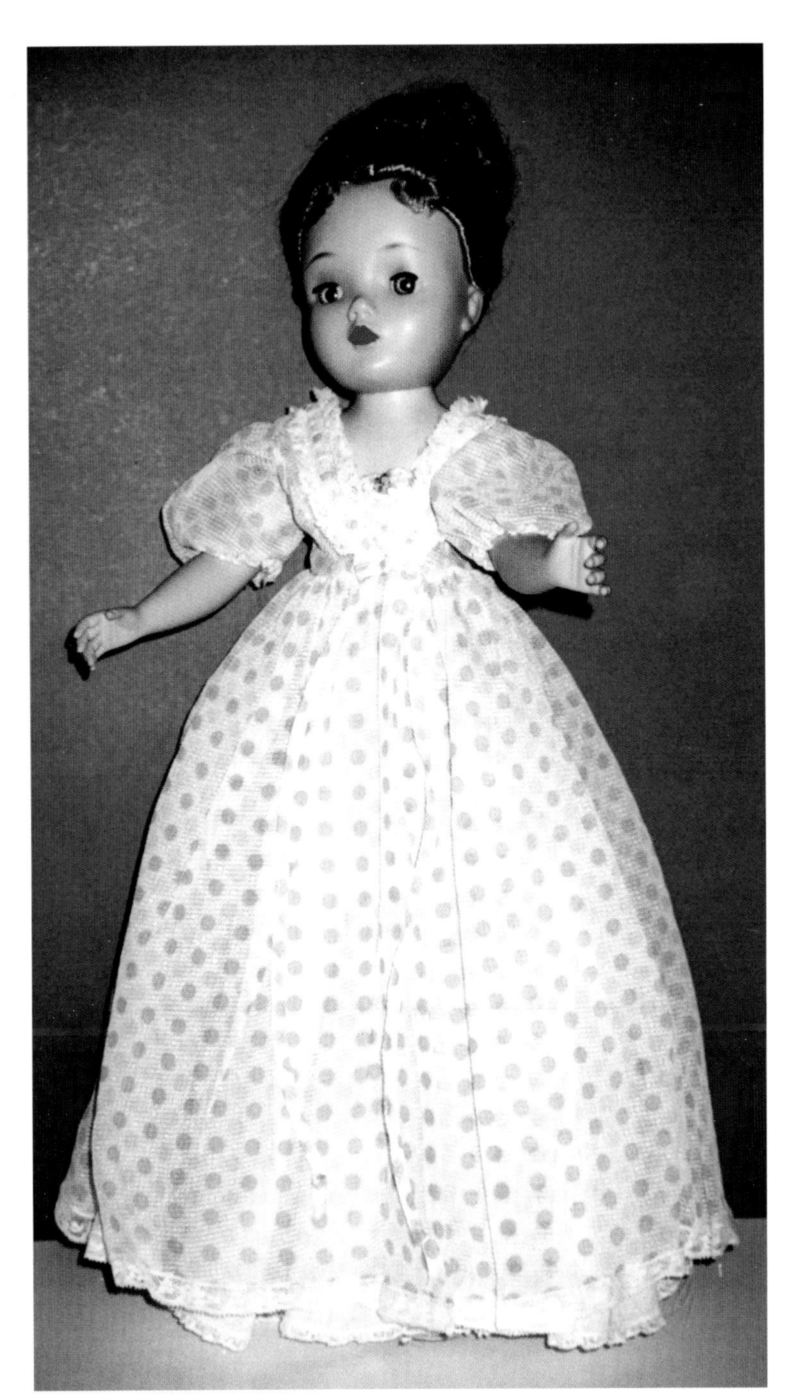

Cissy always had the most elegant sleepwear. Shown here is a lovely lace-trimmed sheer robe. *From the collection of Laura Colpus.*

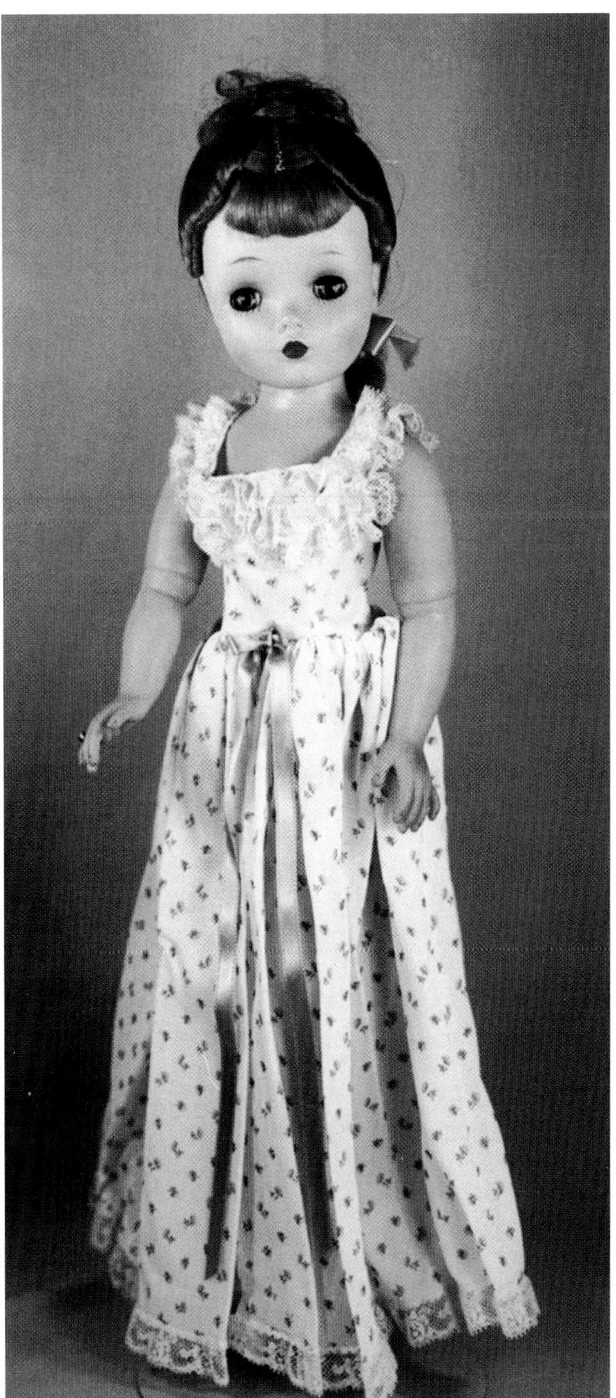

A lace-trimmed tricot nightgown.

Beautiful Cissy peignoir and nightgown.
From the collection of Laura Colpus.

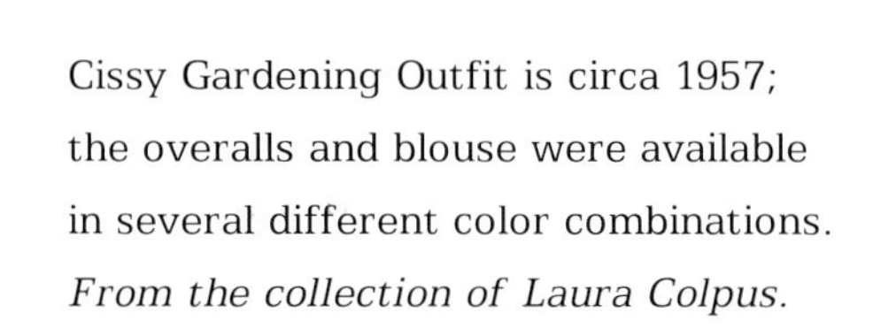

Cissy Gardening Outfit is circa 1957; the overalls and blouse were available in several different color combinations.
From the collection of Laura Colpus.

Even Cissy's pants sets had flair. Shown here is a pair of velvet pants and a matching top with velvet sleeves. *From the collection of Helen Thomas.*

These red corduroy slacks were sold separately and topped here with a white jacket with red embroidered ribbon trim and a mandarin collar. *From the collection of Laura Colpus.*

Another pair of velvet slacks topped with a white cardigan with floral embellishments. *From the collection of Helen Thomas.*

A frilly white organdy blouse with a pair of black velvet slacks and gold belt is an example of mixing pieces from various outfits to create a new look. *From the collection of Laura Colpus.*

This great four-piece set consists of white slacks and top, red jacket, plus a cummerbund type belt. *From the collection of Laura Colpus.*

A navy flannel coat for daywear with a very Mary Poppins look! *From the collection of Laura Colpus.*

A red velvet coat with a straw hat is perfect for daytime jaunts and can be worn without the hat for a grand entrance to the theater. *From the collection of Helen Thomas.*

This Orlon fur swing coat, hat and muff ensemble was a boxed fashion available around 1957. *From the collection of Helen Thomas.*

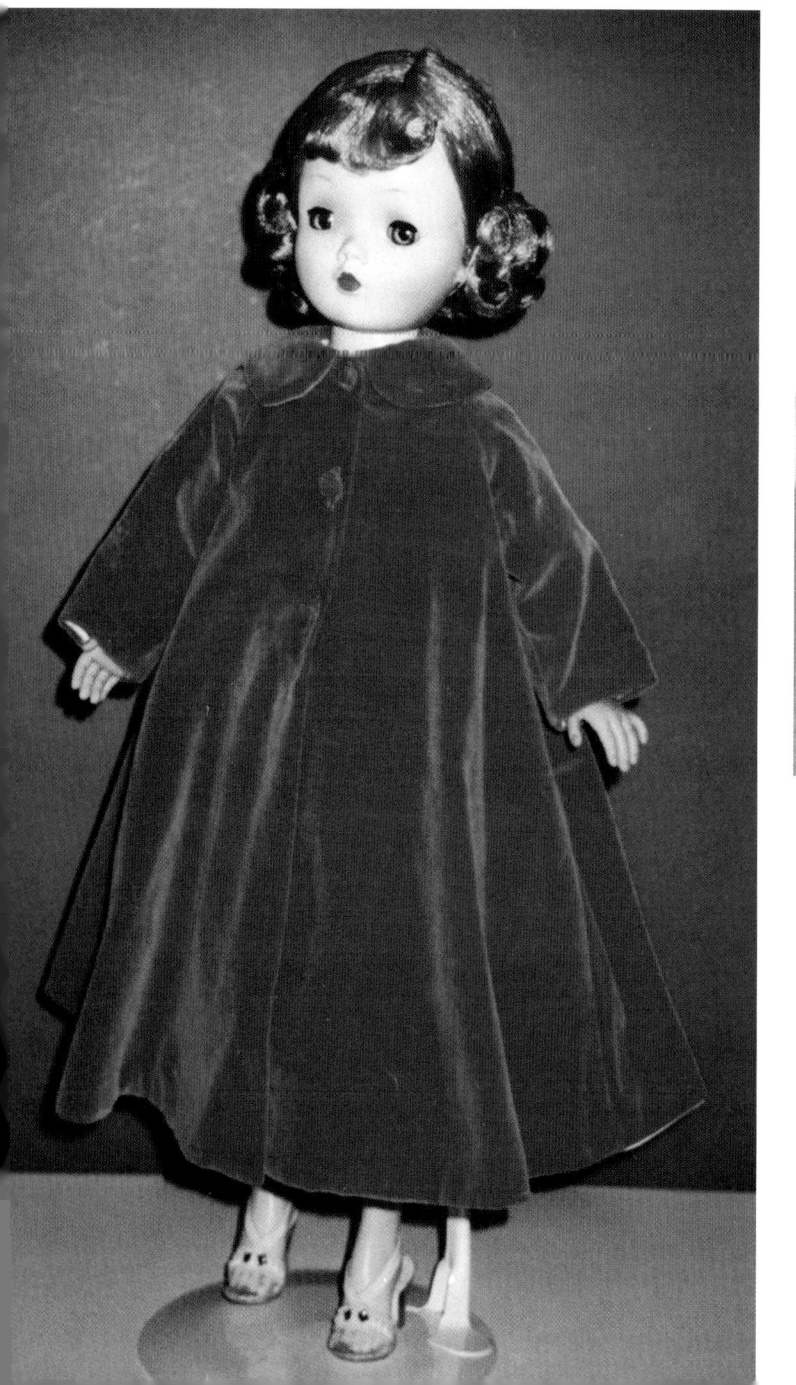

This velvet coat has lots of extra room and is a perfect addition to Cissy's wardrobe. *From the collection of Laura Colpus.*

An elegant white satin full-length opera coat that will cover all of Cissy's ball gowns. *From the collection of Laura Colpus.*

Below: The same set with a different color fur stole and a variation of sunglasses. *From the collection of Helen Thomas.*

Below: A boxed accessory set for Cissy from 1957.

In 1994, Peck Aubry issued this set of Cissy Paper Dolls. The blonde haired doll was dressed in black lingerie and stood 12' tall.

The set included 12 actual Cissy fashions with their correct accessories.

The best part of this set was that it included some of the rarer Cissy fashions, including the "Lissy Cissy" costume. The pink pleated ball gown with gold accents is shown here. There's even a hairpiece included to recreate the actual hairstyle worn by the doll.

Another rare portrait Cissy is the Godey, a pink taffeta gown topped with a purple velvet jacket and bonnet.

Chapter 5

The 1960s—The Decade of Change Begins

As a new decade dawned, once again the Alexander Doll Company catalog distributed to the dealers did not have Cissy on the cover. More interesting was that no Cissy doll was featured inside the catalog either. As the years passed, we as collectors knew that there were some Cissy dolls issued perhaps as store specials in 1960-61, but it was evident that changing tastes working on opposite sides of the spectrum caused some consumer confusion! The Alexander Doll Company and the Ideal Doll Corporation had tremendous success with companion or life size dolls that could wear a children's size 3 and could virtually share a bizarre life with the child. On the other end of the spectrum, Mattel's Barbie® doll was the smash hit of the dubbed "miniature fashion dolls". Eventually, Barbie® won out over the larger size dolls, but in 1960, both genres of dolls were hot. Cissy did have some boxed fashions that year although not illustrated in catalogs, but it was clear the doll was caught in a size war.

Pop culture went through some vast changes as well. Young love competed with the Hollywood vanguard. Elizabeth Taylor won the Oscar for Best Actress in *Butterfield 8* and was hired to star in *Cleopatra* for the then fantastic sum of $1 million plus 10% of the profits. Gladiators and Westerns were sizzling hot. In the movies, Kirk Douglas was *Spartacus* while Marilyn Monroe and Yves Montand starred in *Let's Make Love.* And the industry lost Clark Gable. On television, the top three shows were Westerns—*Gunsmoke, Wagon Train* and *Have Gun Will Travel.*

John F. Kennedy made a successful bid for President in the November elections and the United States demonstrated technological advances by launching 17 satellites and probes. On the music scene, America was twisting with Chubby Checker and The Everly Brothers sang *Cathy's Clown.* Elvis and Connie Francis were still hot and American teens moved to the forefront with an ever-greater culture of their own.

Children started to grow up more quickly, and sophistication and glamour, while still evident in higher-class circles, started to be considered a bit tired.

Opposite page: Very difficult to find is this lilac tulle Cissy from 1961. From the collection of Laura Colpus.

It definitely was a time of change and the dolls certainly reflected the trends of America.

One could never call Madame Alexander someone who didn't constantly come up with new ideas. In a year of yet more transition, the 1961 Alexander Doll Company catalog showed three stunning new Cissy dolls, but as characters and not Cissy herself. Technically, these dolls were Cissy dolls, but in the grand tradition of the Alexander Doll Company, the familiar face of Cissy was used to become new and exciting characters. A Cissy dressed as Scarlett O'Hara is today a very rare and expensive doll. To quote the catalog, "Scarlett O'Hara, an unforgettable doll, right out of the pages of *Gone With the Wind*. A taffeta gown braid trimmed, with matching coat and bonnet, worn over a great billowing crinoline petticoat. Lace mitts and a velvet reticule. Doll 21" tall, fully jointed hard plastic body and head, soft arms. Beautiful patented wig. Scarlett has moving eyes and long curly lashes. A real portrait doll."

To go with Scarlett O' Hara was Melanie, and to quote the catalog, "another *Gone With the Wind* portrait doll, dressed with great elegance in stiff slipper satin with an over-dress of lace. Elaborate hairdo styled in the Godey manner. Expressive moving eyes, long curly lashes, glittering jewels. Melanie is fully jointed, has a hard plastic body and head, soft arms."

Adding to the trilogy was Queen Elizabeth, and once again to quote the catalog, "portrait of a glamorous Queen wearing brocade, decorated with the sash of the garter and garter star. Her twinkling jewels, her shining hair, long gloves and tiara all give her a regal air. Hard plastic body and head, fully jointed doll with soft arms. Moving eyes with long lashes."

Yes, Madame met pop culture and changing times head on with gorgeous dolls that flew in the face of the miniature fashion dolls, namely the Barbie® doll as well as others. One can surmise that the blue-haired grandmothers of the day tried to keep the swirling mass of change from changing their world of department store lunches with well-dressed and well-behaved grandchildren in tow. It mattered little perhaps, to the Saks Fifth Avenue trade that the Supremes signed their contract with Motown. The outside world was encroaching more and more on the tearoom set and their offspring and of course change would eventually overtake even the finest families, but they could ignore some changes. After all, Jacqueline Kennedy was America's first lady and brought an old-world style of elegance back to the White House and was perhaps the last time the world elegance would be used to define the job of being First Lady in some people's eyes.

A beautiful bride, her pleated tulle skirt has a heavy satin overskirt. *From the collection of Helen Thomas.*

A close up view showing the detail on her bodice. *From the collection of Helen Thomas.*

Yet change WAS happening as the youth of America crossed many barriers. African-American groups such as The Shirelles burned up the charts with often overtly sexy songs such as *Will You Still Love Me Tomorrow*. Yet squeaky-clean Ricky Nelson sang *Travelin' Man* to the swooning of the hearts of young America. In films, Doris Day and Rock Hudson as well as Marilyn Monroe, Warren Beatty and Natalie Wood stretched the barriers of cinema in the eyes of many. The year closed with the deaths of Ernest Hemingway and Gary Cooper as well as Grandma Moses at the age of 101.

1961 is long remembered as the year during which tradition was challenged more than ever and even the prerequisite white gloves would pass. The next year brought even more change.

What does one do with a fading house celebrity doll when a REAL celebrity comes on the scene? Madame Alexander had to confront such a decision with Cissy. By 1962, it was evident that Cissy had seen her day. The only time the Cissy face was used in the main catalog was for the Queen Elizabeth II of England, now dressed in a gold brocade gown.

But there were elements of Cissy that still were usable and recognizable. The Cissy body was used (and still is today) with the exception of a new arm (rumored to be bought from American Character Doll Company™...the same arm used on their Sweet Sue Sophisticate® and Toni® doll line). The head mold was a new sculpt and called "Jacqueline" while a 15 inch doll of a little girl called "Caroline" was offered as well. Jacqueline would be the cover doll on the 1962 catalog. This was not a new concept for The Alexander Doll Company. Previously, they had used recognizable faces or bodies to gently steer their customer into uncharted territory. Even Cissy herself had the head mold of a toddler doll from the early 1950s. It was a new day, with new concepts in typical Alexander tradition. The name Cissy was obsolete, although back stock existed in the better stores that carried the doll, and these would continue to bring name recognition for a few more years.

One could say that the clash of cultures constantly created an unstable environment for businesses that had to have product designed at least a year in advance. Previously, change had occurred over decades, now it was accomplished almost overnight. The same world that televised *A Tour of the White House* with an almost Victorian mannered Jacqueline Kennedy competed with hit songs such as *The Peppermint Twist* and the lounge with the same name where white gloves dropped as hemlines rose!

Things changed as a world of single women who thought themselves equal to men began to emerge. In fact, the sexual revolution had just started, at

Sold as a boxed fashion, this dotted tulle ball gown came in several colors in 1960. *From the collection of Helen Thomas.*

Notice the matching red lace gloves and just a splash of contrast with the floral waist corsage. *From the collection of Helen Thomas.*

least out in the open with the publication of *Sex and the Single Girl* by Helen Gurley Brown. The premise was that a single woman did not need herself defined in terms of marriage and motherhood. While daring, it merely told what had perhaps been unspoken for centuries.

On the wide screen, Bette Davis and Joan Crawford starred in *Whatever Happened to Baby Jane?*—basically a modern day Gothic horror movie, and excitement built as the first James Bond film *Dr. No*, starring Sean Connery and Ursula Andress premiered. Television still loved Westerns, but children of the times may remember that possible nuclear war, with the requisite air raids and drill lessons (hands over the head against the wall) were a part of daily life. To add to the changing circumstances of the year, starlet Marilyn Monroe was found dead at age 36 under what today is considered by many to be suspicious circumstances.

The world had changed so much since the debut of Cissy; however, one can see that Madame Alexander was still able to cling to the past through her use of Cissy on the new Jacqueline doll. The gracious past and the confusing future were never in more conflict, yet sales for The Alexander Doll Company remained strong as Madame gathered her talents around what she did best, which was change with the times, while keeping tradition alive. It was an exciting time to be in business and Madame seized the reigns as competently in the early 1960s as she had during The Great Depression.

Still more changes to the doll world came in 1963. The Barbie® doll by Mattel™ was without question Queen of the Prom. Her low price point and high quality fashions made in Japan changed the shape of how a company like The Alexander Doll Company would do business in the future.

Still, Madame Alexander thought that the words "Made in America" meant something to the American consumer at the high-end price point. As history would show, it did not. The Alexander Doll Company was a family-owned business with a location in Harlem, New York. Her factory had a long tradition of hiring local people and training them to do the job. Many employees in the early 1960s were second generation to The Alexander Doll Company.

Regardless, it became more and more apparent with each passing year that miniature fashion dolls, like the Barbie® doll, were the cutting edge. Again, Madame believed the choice of a toy was up to the parent and although television had changed all that with the Saturday morning blitz of commercial after commercial for the latest fad in toys and dolls, the company still had a loyal following and many collectors consider 1963 to be the best of the later years of the company. Sadly, Cissy was not part of the line-up other than

Cissy was slowly fading from the Alexander line up in the 1960s. This Renoir is just one of several portrait dolls Madame created. *From the collection of Ann Rast.*

The Cissy Portrait dolls are very difficult to find. The Godey is from 1961. *From the collection of Ann Rast.*

Queen Elizabeth II. It would be the last time the Cissy head mold in hard plastic would be used. One could say that this was the year that Cissy retired, but she did so as a Queen!

It was a pivotal year. In November, John F. Kennedy was the fourth president to die at the hands of an assassin. Clothing styles were very mixed with actress Tippi Hedren looking like pure class in Alfred Hitchcock's *The Birds*, a kooky film shot with glamour and hairstyles by the famed Alexandre de Paris. Like the patented glamour wigs on Cissy, Tippi took glamour to new heights.

In films, *Tom Jones* took the Oscar, Sidney Poitier took home the Best Actor for *Lilies of the Field* in another barrier breaking moment. *Cleopatra* made its long awaited debut after two years in the making and a production cost of over $40 million, which allegedly almost bankrupted 20th Century Fox. The good news is that the film eventually turned a profit and still is sought after today as a classic. Cary Grant and Audrey Hepburn starred in *Charade*, and on television, *The Beverly Hillbillies* poked fun at the nouveau riche.

Music was at the heart of pop culture and 1963 was a maze of mixed signals with chart-topping songs such as *Go Away Little Girl* by Steve Lawrence, *Walk Like a Man* by The Four Seasons, *Our Day Will Come* by Ruby and the Romantics and *It's My Party* by Lesley Gore. Adding to the cultural mix of the year was Sister Luc-Gabrielle, a.k.a. the Singing Nun, who had a surprise cross over hit with *Dominique*, a song that was even imitated by other recording artists. Television dance shows were more popular than ever with versions in just about every local television market and television sitcoms featured the adventures of the likes of Shelley Fabares, Paul Peterson, Ricky and David Nelson and Don Grady.

While 1963 was a year of tragedy, the events of the year further widen the already spreading gulf between generations as rock stars from England virtually took away the standards that had been set here for decades.

Cissy retired, not as a victim but as a success as The Alexander Doll Company catapulted her fame into other dolls that ended the decade for the company.

The early 1960s will always be remembered as the years of change. Cissy was a doll from the 1950s, but her roots remained until 1963. From a child head mold made during the early 1950s, it is indeed a success story that the face of the 1950s would survive into the turbulent world of the 1960s, similar to Madame herself or course—a survivor. And one could always say the same about Cissy. Like the Phoenix, the doll would resurrect herself once again more than thirty years in the future.

A legacy had begun which was momentarily retired...

Another Cissy Portrait from the 1960s. Some say she is Melanie. *From the collection of Helen Thomas.*

The Melanie Portrait from 1961, #2235. She has a very elaborate hairstyle and extra long lashes. *From the collection of Helen Thomas.*

Scarlett Portrait circa 1961-1962. *From the collection of Ann Rast.*

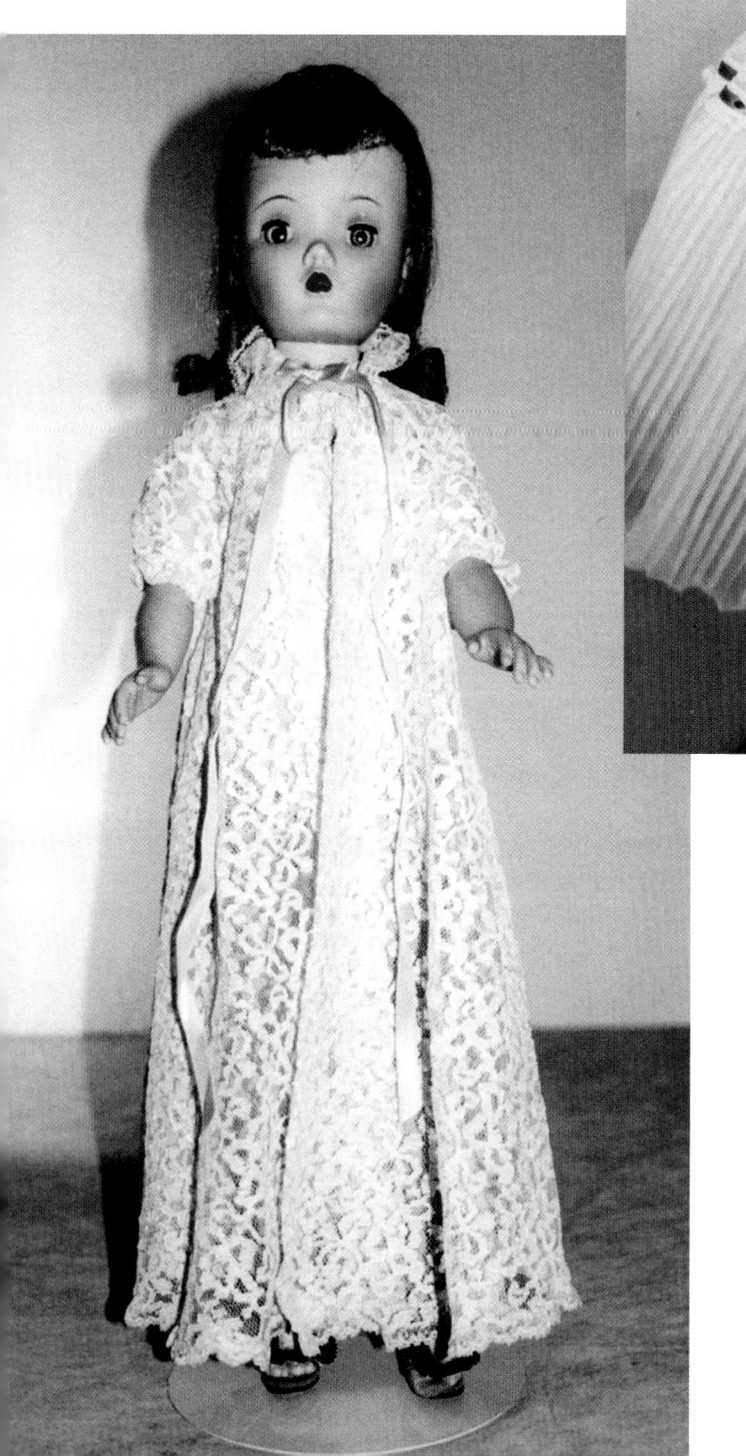

This lace robe was sold in 1960 as a boxed fashion, it is #22-26. *From the collection of Helen Thomas.*

There were very few boxed fashions available for Cissy in 1960. Most were leftover from 1959. This sateen skirt with a taffeta belt and white top was one of the last outfits produced. *From the collection of Laura Colpus*

The Ice Capades ice show used Cissy as a model for their costumes in the late 1950s through the early 1960s. The costumes were not made by Madame Alexander. They are one-of-a-kind and are very rare. *From the collection of Helen Thomas.*

Chapter 6

The 1990s— The Legend Returns

A retro sixties movement defined the early 1990s. Teenagers on the street looked like twins of those during the 1960s. By 1994, things turned around and the emphasis was on the early 1970s as the children of that era came of age and wanted to recapture their memories. It was an amazing time as home computers started to make inroads into the average American home and the influence of the 1960s continued until the mid-1990s.

Cissy was the dream doll of America and had been for half a century. Be it retro or contemporary, she was the ultimate and most expensive of the fashion doll genre, but the early 1990s Cissy dolls just didn't appeal to the market. You could say that the doll was ahead of her time since the fashion doll boom had yet to take hold of the doll-collecting world. In addition, the Alexander Doll Company did not use the name or concept of Cissy in their marketing to it's fullest potential. Cissy was retired again, but not for long.

The cover of the Alexander Doll Company catalog in 1996 featured the return of Cissy! This was "A-list" news at Toy Fair and the press gathered around to see the new offerings. Once again, the same body was used as in 1961 with the straight arms and the head mold was an exact replica of the hard plastic mold, but this time it was in vinyl. The real story, however, was the clothing. Alexander had pulled out all the stops with six new Cissy dolls plus a dazzling African-American version. Dealers were ecstatic and sales were through the roof! One could honestly say that it was like a movie legend had returned. After four decades, Cissy had come home to a different world.

Things had changed a great deal. Movies like *Twister* and *Independence Day* had state of the art special effects, while period movies swept the Oscars with *The English Patient*. Wives were given the message, "Don't get mad; get everything" in *The First Wives Club*. Some special stars passed away such as Dean Martin and Claudette Colbert. Cissy was in good company coming from New York. It was the biggest attendance in years on Broadway. Yet more changes lay ahead for America's dream doll.

Opposite page: Enchanted Evening was produced as a Portrait doll from 1991-1992 and uses the new vinyl head Cissy.

Lilac Fairie Ballerina was a second Portrait doll using the Cissy vinyl head. She was made from 1993-1994.

A close up of the ballerina, she was very detailed.

Cissy's back! Coral and Leopard Travel Ensemble was part of the new MA Couture Cissy debut in 1996.

Vinyl head, modern make-up, Cissy returned in a big way.

In 1997, Cissy returned with a floral retro 1940s theme. One could almost picture Rita Hayworth on her beach chair with a very pre-World War II hairstyle wearing Daisy Resort. The Platinum dealer exclusive, Calla Lily Evening Column Cissy was a smash hit but the star doll for this year was the Cissy's Secret Armoire, loosely based on the Victoria's Secret Lingerie campaign. Gardenia Gala Cissy was very retro and would have made Madame Alexander proud. It proved to be another good year for Cissy.

Heroines were certainly in style as the film *Titanic* caused box office frenzy. It was the most expensive film ever made with a price tag of approximately $200 million! Like Cissy, the strongest character was a young woman, played by Kate Winslet in love with teen idol Leonardo di Caprio. *Star Wars* was re-released and grossed over $35 million. Actor Jimmy Stewart passed away on July 2nd. Television was still obsessed with *ER* and *Seinfeld*. And while Cissy was the darling of the doll world, once again beaming down from glass showcases, it was a totally different world. Heaven's Gate cult members had a mass suicide and two men were convicted of the 1993 bombing at The World Trade Center. It is interesting to compare the world of the 1950s with that of the present and to note that Cissy is still able to command a presence in a very, very different world than those of the Eisenhower years.

By 1998, the Cissy doll legend grew as new collectors entered the hobby It was no longer necessary to relate current events or history to the theme of the dolls. Cissy took a ride on the Orient Express, often considered the most lavish and expensive Cissy dolls to date. Seven new styles were offered and the prices were more than $500. It was obvious that the doll was not being marketed to children. That is not to say that a doll here or there was not bought for a child, but the price point and the detail of the dolls led one to believe that this was a doll for collectors, produced in a limited quantity and not marketed for children.

While the Orient Express was the selection of the Alexander design team, it is interesting to note current events for the year. *Shakespeare in Love* won the Oscar, as did Gywneth Paltrow for the same movie. Television legend Oprah Winfrey starred in the film *Beloved*, the movie *Lost in Space* played off the hit 1960s television series and it was the year that legends Frank Sinatra and Robert Young passed away. As Cissy took a glamour trip like never before, the White House was involved in a scandal while the United States balanced it's budget for the first time in 30 years. Matthew Shepherd was fatally beaten to death and hate crimes gained national attention. One could easily see that the real world and the fantasy world had grown further and

Ebony and Ivory Houndstooth Suit was also issued in an African American version in 1996. Dog by Annalee Doll Company.

Café Rose and Ivory Cocktail Dress is shown here in the hard-to-find African American version. She was also available as a Caucasian doll.

further apart. Collectors were eager to see Cissy take a ride on the Orient Express, as the collection at wholesale was a sellout.

In 1999, Cissy was all about American Fashion design. At Toy Fair in February, dealers and the media (no longer the press) were dazzled by 21 new Cissy dolls. Orders were hot and heavy but later it was revealed that only 10 of the dolls would be made and that the Arnold Scassi Cissy would be exclusive to the Danbury Mint™. Later in the year, three other Cissy dolls from the original collection were produced, but the most popular doll among on-line collector groups was the Betsey Johnson Cissy doll. With pink hair and the popular slip dress, she was light years away from the Cissy doll of the 1950s. For reasons unknown, this doll was never produced. She did spawn a host of doll artists either selling the wig or redoing the doll. But, Cissy was an expensive doll to redo with a wholesale cost of around $250.

The year 1999 was very interesting. The film *American Beauty* took the Oscar, while Hillary Swank in a transgender role won best actress for *Boys Don't Cry*. *The Sixth Sense* with its startling ending mesmerized moviegoers and Tim Burton scared audiences with *Sleepy Hollow*. Sadly, the year began with an impeachment trial against President Clinton, but he was ultimately acquitted. Columbine High School saw violence and John F. Kennedy Jr., with his wife and sister-in-law are killed in a plane crash. It was a memorable year. One could say that it was ironic that the dolls no longer reflected pop culture, but fantasy, although one could say that perhaps that was always true!

The year 2000 was touted as the new Millennium although according to many authorities with statistics to back it up, it was neither the start of the new millennium, the new decade or the new century. Doom and gloom stories about computer shutdowns and a world turned upside down never happened thankfully. In an ironic twist, this year, yet still undefined by experts, carried one word and that was retro. With nothing really new to offer anyone except a computer programmer, the past became the present.

For Cissy, that meant new skin tones, fresh hairstyles, and dazzling costumes, which took Cissy back to new heights of glamour. Cissy had a very good year, as new items like shoe accessory sets sold out quickly. It was a great time for ethnic Cissy dolls; they finally took off with record sales. One could say that the doll had come full circle. While the dolls from the 1950s to the early 1960s were about a sitcom life, the dolls of the present were multi-racial and steeped in the thought that a new century meant a new way of looking at glamour. Actresses like Halle Berry proved that fact. And at the Oscars, *Gladiator* won for best film. The entertainment world said good-bye

Aquamarine Evening Column and Coat was also part of the Cissy debut in 1996.

Aquamarine without her coat.

to Steve Allen, Walter Matthau and Hedy Lamar. The so-called Internet "dot-com" boom began to backslide and computer hackers introduced more sophisticated computer viruses.

Everything was new about 2001. The Oscar winning film was *A Beautiful Mind* and Halle Berry was the first African American woman to win Best Actress, which she won for *Monster's Ball*. The Tony Awards got a record 12 trophies and *Harry Potter and Sorcerer's Stone* made $93.5 million on its first weekend. And there was a new political agenda as George W. Bush was sworn in as the 43rd President on January 25th. The year got off to a great start.

At Toy Fair, Cissy was again retro and more glamorous than ever. Looking like movie icons of the Golden Age of Hollywood, glamorous ball gowns were introduced that rivaled the dolls that stood on the staircases of the Alexander showroom on Fifth Avenue decades before.

One has to close the year 2001 with a mention of the September 11th destruction of the World Trade Center and the attack on the Pentagon. No single event had ever brought Americans closer. The Alexander Doll Company issued a special Cissy in patriotic colors.

In the year 2002, Cissy is still in a glamorous state of mind. Some of the very limited dolls designed by independent contractors sell out at wholesale quickly. Accessories like trunk sets with wigs and shoe accessory sets seem to be what the collector wants. It looks like a great year for Cissy and for doll collecting. A legend has returned and never looked better!

Onyx Velvet Lace Gala Gown and Coat.

Pearl Embroidered Lace Bridal Gown was not your traditional bridal gown, issued in 1996.

Red Sequin Gown was the last of the 1996 Cissy dolls. She was harder to locate since she was only available to select retailers.

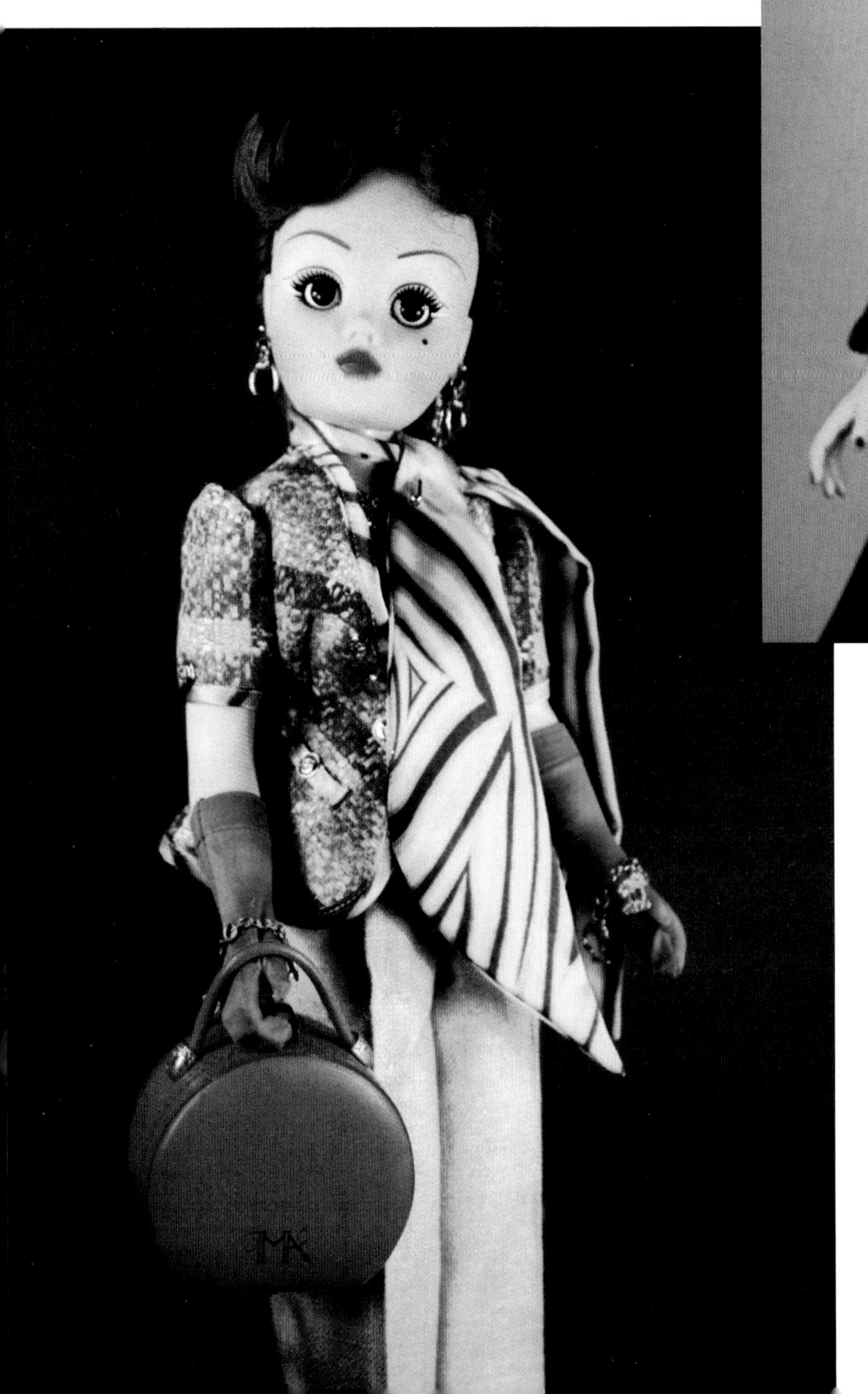

The 1997 Cissy Collection was a floral theme with 1940s style as shown by this Daisy Resort Ensemble.

The Tea Rose Cocktail Ensemble could be purchased as an African American or Caucasian doll.

Daisy Resort also included this retro bathing suit and lounge chair.

Gardenia Gala Ball Gown has layers of tulle under her satin dress and is accented with gardenias on the back.

The Peony and Butterfly Wedding Gown was the 1997 Cissy bride.

Calla Lily Column and Bolero is so detailed with it's fully beaded gown.

Cissy's Secret Armoire was introduced in 1997 and sold through 1998. This set is getting very difficult to find.

Madame Butterfly was not officially part of the Cissy line in 1997.

The Cissy face is perfect for this stunning doll.

Paris Cissy was produced in 1998 as part of Cissy traveling on the Orient Express.

Barcelona Cissy was available as both an African American and a Caucasian doll.

Not only was the entire front of Barcelona's dress embroidered but her shawl was embroidered and had long black crocheted fringe.

The Venice Cissy from 1997 was definitely ready for Carnival with her heavily jeweled elephant mask.

Below: Beneath her satin cape, Venice is wearing a bright gown and carries a jeweled fan.

Below: One could easily see why the 1998 collection retailed for $590! The jewels, accessories, and additional pieces of clothing were well worth the price.

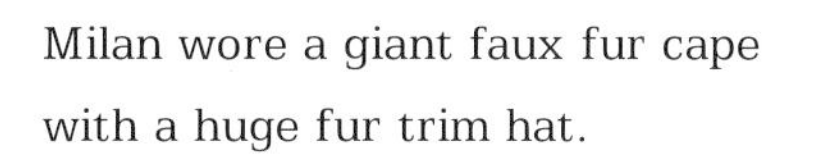

Milan wore a giant faux fur cape with a huge fur trim hat.

Under her cape was a faux fur jacket topping a satin miniskirt.

Budapest Cissy is an interesting mix of pieces of clothing that combine in various ways to create a number of different looks. Here, the velvet and faux fur bolero combined with a velvet skirt and the faux fur hat, creates an amazing coat ensemble.

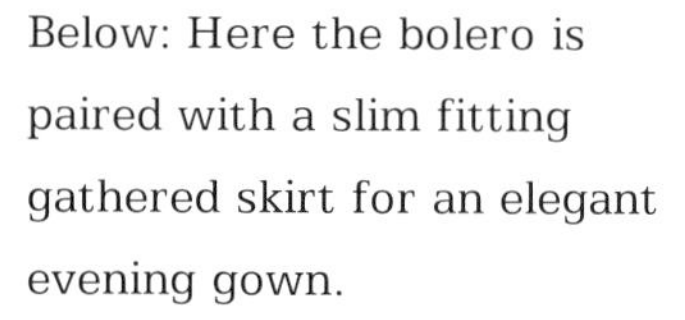

Below: Here the bolero is paired with a slim fitting gathered skirt for an elegant evening gown.

Below: The blue velvet mini dress is topped with a rhinestone and fringed overlay for a great flapper style cocktail dress.

This Cissy was called Madame Alexander Celebrates American Design and she was designed by the company's designers and based on Cissy's torso gowns from the 1950s.

This Cissy was designed by Jessica McClintock, best known for her romantic style.

Ultimate Angel was produced from 1998-1999. She was not part of the Cissy Couture, but equally as beautiful.

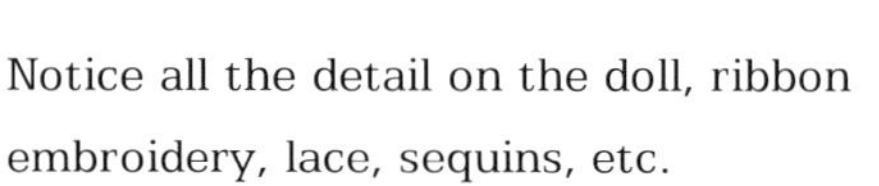

Notice all the detail on the doll, ribbon embroidery, lace, sequins, etc.

The 1999 Cissy Collection was all created by American fashion designers. The Fernando Sanchez Cissy was featured on the cover of the catalog.

The Sanchez Cissy is shown here without her coat and bubble head dress.

The Anna Sui Cissy has a Scandinavian flair to her outfit.

This emerald green suit by Dana Buchman looks great on this auburn-haired Cissy.

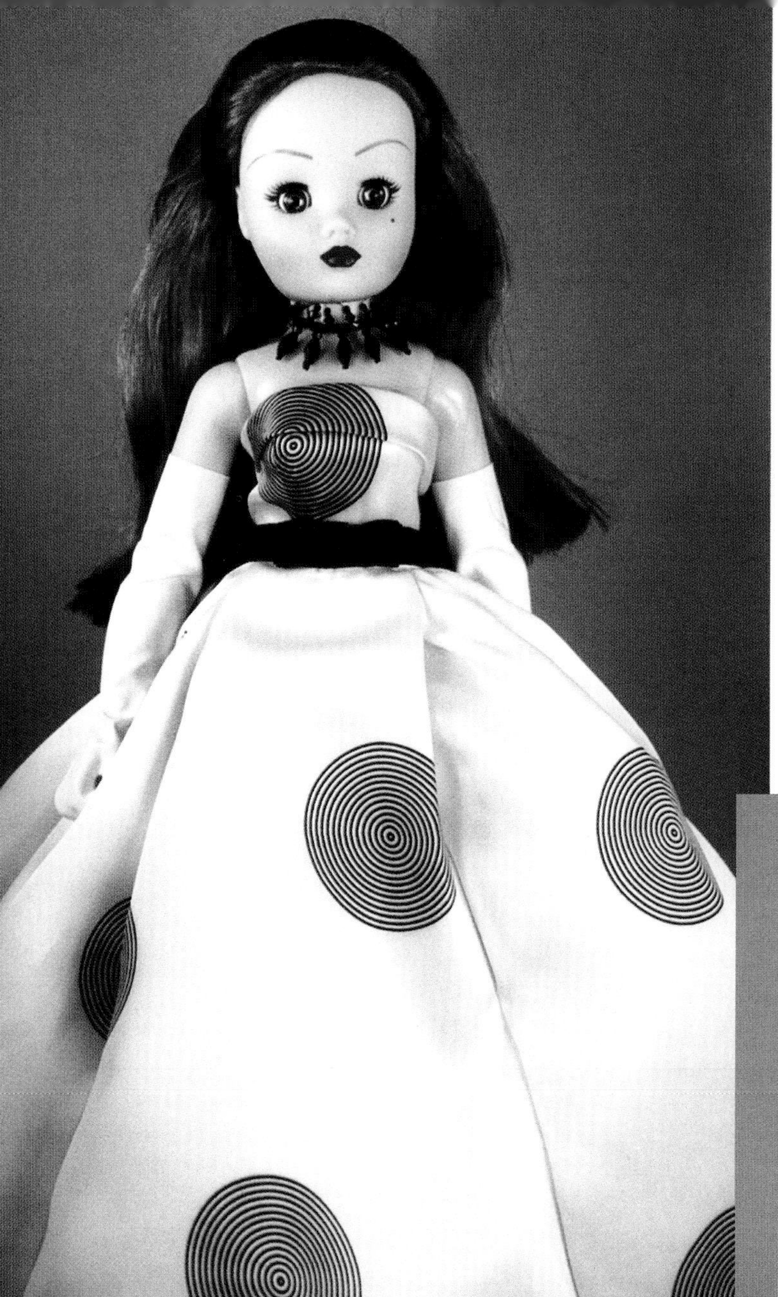

The James Purcell Cissy was a simple ball gown with a very retro print.

The doll's necklace looks great, but unfortunately should not be used. It stains the vinyl.

Badgley Mischka created this lace and sequin column for Cissy.

This New York City inspired ensemble was designed by Linda Allard for Ellen Tracy.

Josie Natori, best known for elegant lingerie, created this organdy lounging pajama set.

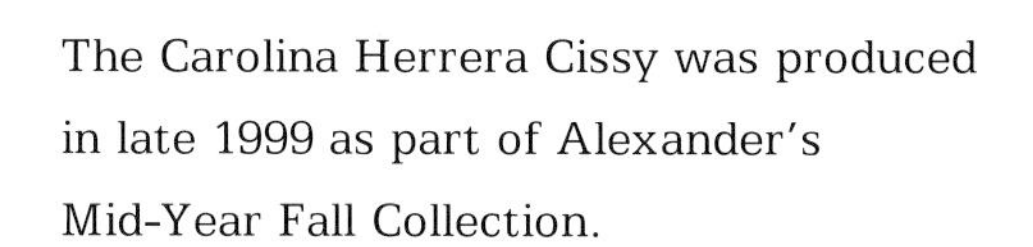

The Carolina Herrera Cissy was produced in late 1999 as part of Alexander's Mid-Year Fall Collection.

Mark Bouwer designed the only African American Cissy produced in 1999.

The Holiday Cissy was introduced in Alexander's 1999 Winter Preview Collection and sold out quickly.

Cissy travels again in 2000, this time visiting various places around the world. This is the New York Cissy, ready for an evening gala.

Shanghai Cissy is wearing a very modern suit in a Chinese brocade fabric. *From the collection of Laura Colpus.*

Cairo Cissy used a new skin tone to create a more exotic look. She is shown here in her bathing suit. *From the collection of Laura Colpus.*

Just like the 1950s, a long skirt is added with a sash, and Cairo's bathing suit becomes a ball gown. *From the collection of Laura Colpus.*

Yardley Cissy was announced late in 2000 and sold out immediately. Only 750 dolls were made and she is getting harder to find.

Atlanta Stroll Scarlett was the first Scarlett in over 30 years to have the Cissy face. She was a limited edition made only in 2000.

The 2001 Cissy dolls were a return to the past. The Black and White Ball Cissy is reminiscent of the torso gowns Cissy wore in the 1950s.

Society Stroll Cissy was offered as both African American and Caucasian in 2001.

Haute Couture Cissy makes a statement in her black suit with just a touch of white.

Royal Reception Cissy's outfit is an updated version of a ball gown worn by the Maid of Honor dolls made in the 1950s.

On the Avenue Cissy is the second doll inspired by the Yardley of London print ads of the 1950s.

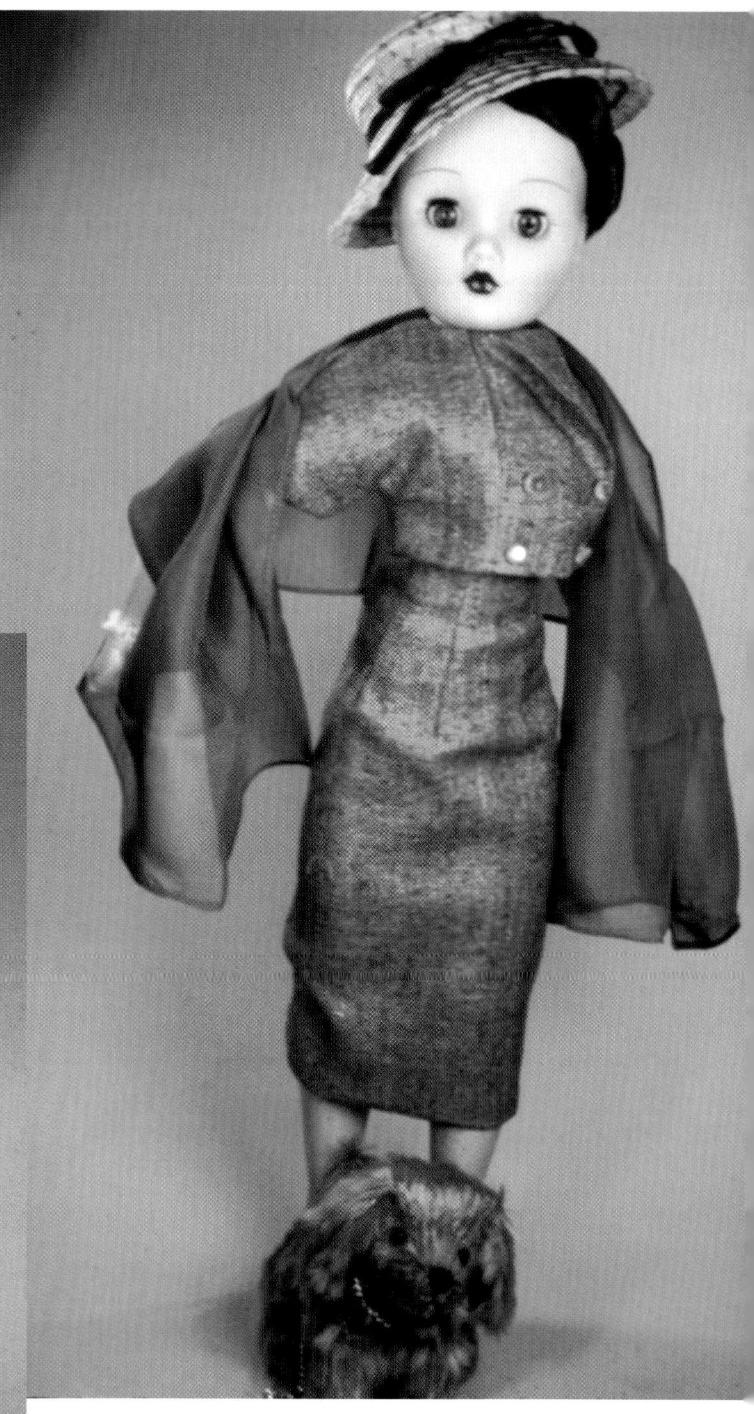

America the Beautiful Cissy was one of the patriotic themed dolls issued late in 2001.

Madame Du Pompadour Cissy was ultra limited to 100 dolls and retailed for $1700! *From the collection of Ann Rast.*

Another ultra limited doll in 2001 was Prima Donna Cissy. Only 100 dolls were produced. *From the collection of Ann Rast.*

Chapter 7

Exclusive Cissy Dolls

Everyone loves something exclusive and doll collectors are no exception to the rule! The Alexander Doll Company has had a long relationship with doing dolls for select stores and businesses, especially F.A.O. Schwarz. Just like other "exclusives" in life, the price point doesn't necessarily have to be higher, but the item is unique in some way.

With dolls, exclusives are usually made in a very low number and can also be for an event such as a luncheon or convention, or even for recognition by The Alexander Doll Company for outstanding sales achievement. Some Cissy dolls have been made just for dealers who have achieved a certain level of sales. These dolls of course are very hard to locate since many dealers do not participate in this program.

Store exclusives can be tricky as well. Recently, a very low edition of less than 40 pieces of a Cissy was made for F.A.O. Schwarz and sold out before most collectors even got the catalog! The collector of this sort of doll (and some specialize only in this type of Cissy) has to be well-connected and networking constantly to stay in the loop of things so that as new dolls become available, they can be instantly ordered. It isn't enough to stay in touch with your favorite doll shop, because you won't find other exclusives there.

Ideally, one tries to buy event dolls at the issue price. If one has not attended the event, then having a contact who is attending the event is a good idea. Actually, the worst time to buy an exclusive is right after the event. After an event, the Internet is a flutter about the doll, online auctions are flooded with dolls and prices are usually high (it IS a good time to sell though). With minor exceptions, the exclusive starts to drop to a realistic price about a year after the event and then can either go gradually up in year two or continue to drop. Since a low number means fewer dolls, it can be risky to wait if it is a doll that you desperately want.

Yes, the word exclusive conjures up many things, but in the world of Cissy it usually means a first class and desirable doll.

Opposite page: One of the first exclusive modern Cissy dolls was this 1998 Miss St. John. It was a limited edition for Neiman-Marcus Department Stores.

Arnold Scassi Cissy was one of the designs featured in the 1999 Cissy line but it became an exclusive for the Danbury Mint™.

A close-up of the Arnold Scassi Cissy showing her elaborate jewelry and hair style.

The Lilly Pulitzer Cissy was the only other American designer Cissy produced. She was ultra limited to 25 dolls and was made for the Madame Alexander Doll Club Convention's Cissy Event in 1999.

This coordinating bathing suit came with the Lilly Pulitzer Cissy. She is one of the most sought after Cissy dolls ever made.

Another hard-to-find Cissy is this Fortune Teller. She was made as an exclusive for the Collector's United Gathering in 1999. Only 180 dolls were made for the event.

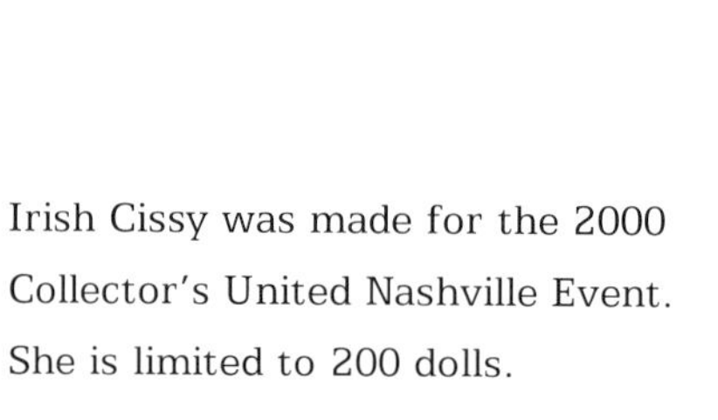

Irish Cissy was made for the 2000 Collector's United Nashville Event. She is limited to 200 dolls.

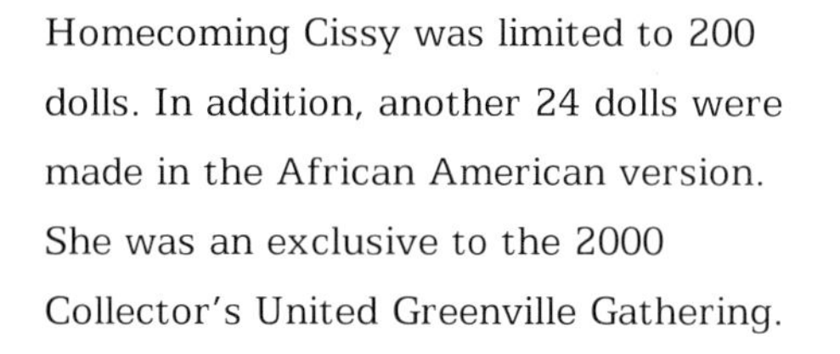

Homecoming Cissy was limited to 200 dolls. In addition, another 24 dolls were made in the African American version. She was an exclusive to the 2000 Collector's United Greenville Gathering.

Cissy Gala was a limited edition of 300 dolls for the Madame Alexander Doll Club Convention's Cissy Event in 2000. The same doll with blonde hair and a lavender dress was produced in a limited edition of 30 dolls and used as a centerpiece doll for the event.

The 2001 Cissy Scarlett is a remake of the 1960s Cissy Scarlett. She was a limited edition of 200 dolls for the Collector's United Gathering.

Blue Danube Cissy is a limited edition of 200 Caucasian and 6 African American dolls for the 2001 Collector's United Nashville Event.

Cissy Evening at the Pops was made for the Madame Alexander Doll Club Convention's Cissy Event in 2001 and is limited to 310 dolls.

Cissy Diva was the centerpiece doll at the 2001 Madame Alexander Doll Club Convention's Cissy Event. She is ultra limited to approximately 35 dolls.

June Bride Cissy is the 2002 Madame Alexander Doll Club Convention's Cissy Event Doll. She was limited to 300 dolls. *From the collection of Laura Colpus.*

June Bridesmaid Cissy was the centerpiece doll at the 2002 Madame Alexander Doll Club Convention's Cissy Event. She is ultra limited to 40 dolls. *From the collection of Laura Colpus.*

Chapter 8

Cissy and F.A.O. Schwarz

The Alexander Doll Company has always had a warm relationship with the legendary New York City toy store, F.A.O. Schwarz. So, it would be natural that Madame Alexander with her love of the upper classes and prestige would gravitate to a toy store with the cache of F.A.O. Schwarz. Scarcely is a child alive (young or old) that doesn't feel a tingle when the name F.A.O. Schwarz is mentioned.

The namesake of the world famous toy chain, Frederick August Otto Schwarz, founded the business in 1862, an amazing six years after he arrived in America from Westphalia, Germany. Originally, he opened his business in Baltimore, Maryland until 1870 when he decided to move to the more prestigious New York City where he opened the Schwarz Toy Bazaar on Broadway. Enlisting the help of his three brothers, he was able to capitalize on the connections that they had with Europe's finest toy sources. Because of these connections and Frederick's good taste, he was soon known as THE source for high end and unusual toys, many exclusive to his shop. In 1880, he moved to larger quarters in New York's Union Square. At the time, that was considered to be the fashionable shopping center housing prestigious merchants and stores such as Tiffany and others.

F.A.O. eventually moved to two other New York locations before moving uptown in 1931 to 745 Fifth Avenue. Considered to be the flagship store, it remained at this location until 1986 when the store moved across the street to 767 Fifth Avenue. Today the store has other flagship stores in Chicago, San Francisco, Las Vegas and Orlando among other places.

Madame Alexander was attracted to the upward mobility of a store dealing in exclusives. Unfortunately, the only primary resource materials for F.A.O. store specials are the F.A.O. catalogs and even then, not all specials were listed. Cissy certainly was not the first doll to be featured as an F.A.O. special, but documentation exists of lavish Cissy dolls in trunks that featured high-end lingerie, fur stoles and jewelry. Much the same way the Cissy dolls of today are considered the high end of the fashion doll spectrum, the vintage dolls were considered the cream of the crop by parents and children alike.

The 1955 F.A.O. Schwarz catalog featured 3 dolls and 4 individual outfits for Cissy. In addition, one could purchase only a crinoline slip or a set of shoes with stockings.

WHEN ORDERING FROM CATALOG, BE SURE TO STATE ITEM NAME AND NUMBER, COLOR AND SIZE WHERE NEEDED, AND SHIPPING WEIGHT AND PRICE.

CISSY THE DEBUTANTE DOLL Not a baby doll, but a new 20" young lady with a slim, delicately ... and beautifully shaped feet that wear only high-heeled shoes. Her head, body and ... of hard, high-quality plastic while her jointed arms are of soft plastic. Cissy's head can be posed in life-like positions and she can walk. Her beautiful saran coiffure further accen... "grown up" look.

A 16-28 CISSY IN UNDIES Ship. wt. 4 lbs. ... $13.95
... panties, bra, stockings and slippers. NEGLIGEE NOT INCLUDED. See below.
25-370 NYLON NEGLIGEE ... $3.75

B 26-43 CISSY IN DINNER GOWN Ship. wt. 7 lbs. ... $25.00
... gown, with rhinestone-trimmed bodice, ostrich feathers fans, bracelet and rhinestone ring.

C 16-40 CISSY AS QUEEN ELIZABETH Ship. wt. 7 lbs. ... $25.00
... gown of white brocade, with garter sash and star, long white gloves, and tiara, earrings and ... jeweled with rhinestones.

D 25-372 LINED VELVET COAT & HAT. rose ... $6.00
E 25-355 CAN-CAN PETTICOAT. red and white ... $2.75
...OT FULL-LENGTH NIGHTIE. pink ... $3.00
...HEELED SHOES & NYLON STOCKINGS ... $1.50
...PIQUE STRIPED SUN DRESS ... $3.75
...SIA AND WHITE PRINT AFTERNOON DRESS ... $4.00

...ZE SWEET SUE. Ship. wt. 10 lbs. Express only ... $29.95
...ized beauty, stands 31" tall. Her dimpled vinyl arms and legs are ... moved to many life-like positions. She can sit, bend, kneel and walk. ... be washed, combed or curled to look best with her outfit — an adorable ... fitted coat with full skirt and white collar and cuffs, red velvet ... bonnet and bag, taffeta dress under coat, and undies.
... 25" tall. Ship. wt. 8 lbs. ... $10.00
... 18" tall. Ship. wt. 6 lbs. ... $13.95
... 15" tall. Ship. wt. 5 lbs. ... $11.95

L 16-51 MISS MOPPET WITH BRIDAL WARDROBE ... $12.95
"Miss Moppet" is a charming 11" plastic doll, fully jointed, with moving eyes and saran wig. She wears a red and black striped shopping dress complete with purse and straw hat. Also packed in the striped heavy cardboard suitcase are her elaborate bridal outfit, a smart travel suit with accessories, a dainty blue taffeta party dress with matching panties, lace-trimmed poke hat and bag, three-piece striped sunsuit and beach hat and full-length nightie and robe. Shoes and socks for each outfit included. Ship. wt. 5 lbs.

31

A 25-1 WENDY BABY WITH BOTTLE ... $3.00
A new 7½" vinyl-bodied drinking and wetting doll, cute as a button, with movable arms and legs, and eyes that open and close. Bonnet covers her close-cropped hair. Trainer panties and booties included. Ship. wt. 1 lb.
25-2 WENDY BABY IN CHRISTENING DRESS (Not Illustrated) ... $6.50
B 25-21 ROMPER & CAP ... $2.25
C 25-31 FLANNELETTE ROBE ... $1.50
D 25-26 BATISTE NIGHTIE ... $1.50
E 25-3 CHRISTENING COAT AND BONNET ... $3.50
F 25-5 ORGANDY DRESS, BONNET, SLIP & PANTIES ... $3.50
25-11 CHECK GINGHAM DRESS, BONNET, SLIP & PANTIES (Not illus.) ... $3.50
25-12 BLUE DOTTED SWISS DRESS, BONNET, SLIP & PANTY (Not illus.) ... $3.50

G 26-3 CISSY, THE DEBUTANTE DOLL ... $16.95
A 20" young lady doll with molded figure, beautifully dressed in pink and white polished cotton dress, black velvet beret and high-heeled shoes. Ship. wt. 5 lbs.
16-28 CISSY IN UNDIES ... $13.95
(Not illus.) Ship. wt. 5 lbs.
H 25-378 PRINT SUN DRESS ... $3.75
J 25-398 CARDIGAN ... $2.75
K 25-381 RED FAILLE SKIRT ... $3.00
L 25-355 CAN CAN PETTICOAT ... $2.75
M 25-371 AFTERNOON DRESS ... $4.00
N 25-370 NYLON HOUSECOAT ... $3.75
P 25-363 TRICOT NIGHTIE ... $3.00

R 25-50 WENDY-DOLL ... $2.25
Here is the new Wendy, an attractive 8" walking doll with jointed knees (so she can sit gracefully, of course) moving arms, washable hair and eyes that open and close. Dressed in the bare essentials of panties and footwear. For additional clothing, see below. Ship wt. 1 lb.
S 25-86 RED-STRIPED ORGANDY DRESS, STRAW HAT, SLIP & PANTIES ... $3.50
T 25-87 SILK PAJAMAS WITH LACE TRIM ... $1.25
U 25-91 TERRYCLOTH BEACH OUTFIT ... $2.75
V 25-93 BRIDAL OUTFIT ... $4.50
W 25-98 TENNIS OUTFIT ... $2.00
Y 25-99 LACE-TRIMMED ROBE ... $1.25
(Not Illustrated)
25-16 GABARDINE COAT, HAT & DRESS ... $3.50

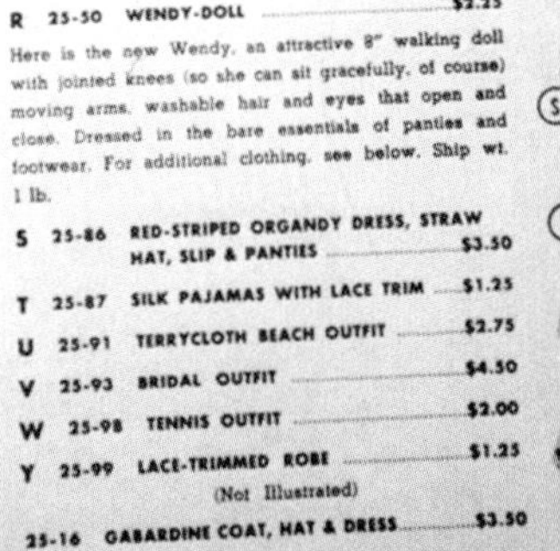

28

F.A.O. Schwarz used to issue catalogs for summer toys. While the catalog primarily consisted of swing sets, pool toys and other sporting goods, dolls were featured as a rainy day activity. This 1956 summer catalog includes two Cissy dolls plus various individual fashions.

Madame Alexander Dolls

CISSY, THE DEBUTANTE DOLL Not a baby doll, but a 20" young lady with a slim, delicately molded figure and beautifully shaped feet that wear only high-heeled shoes. Her head, body and jointed legs are of hard, high-quality plastic, while her jointed arms are of soft plastic. Cissy's head can be posed in life-like positions and she can walk. Her beautiful saran coiffure further accentuates her "grown-up" look.

A 26-79 CISSY IN EVENING GOWN Wt. 7 lbs. 25.00
Blue satin gown with cascading side drape over a billowy taffeta petticoat. Smart shoulder cape of orlon nutria is satin lined. Jeweled earrings and ring

B 26-32 CISSY IN BRIDAL GOWN Ship. wt. 7 lbs. 25.00
White tulle gown has pleated skirt, lace bodice and satin sash pulled through loop of pearls. Medici cap has chapel length veil. Bridal bouquet, pearl necklace and ring

C 26-25 CISSY AS QUEEN ELIZABETH 25.00
Court gown of white brocade, worn over taffeta hoop petticoat, with sash of the Garter with star, long white gloves, and tiara, earrings and bracelets jeweled with rhinestones. Ship. wt. 7 lbs.

D 26-15 CISSY IN COCKTAIL DRESS 17.95
Ship. wt. 7 lbs.
Smart blue taffeta long torso dress, worn over can-can petticoat. Separate velvet bolero, tiny veiled hat of flowers, rhinestone bracelet and afternoon bag.

E 26-9 CISSY IN AFTERNOON DRESS 17.95
Ship. wt. 7 lbs.
Stylish red dotted Swiss organdy dress worn over white taffeta can-can petticoat that rustles when she walks. Smart veiled straw hat trimmed with flowers. Hatbox included.

F 26-20 CISSY IN UNDIES 13.95
In lace chemise, stockings and flowered mules. NEGLIGEE NOT INCLUDED. See below. Wt. 5 lbs.

25-22 LACE TRIMMED COTTON NEGLIGEE (as Ill. on Cissy) 3.75

G 25-28 SLACKS WITH FLOWERED CARDIGAN 4.00

H 25-9 COTTON NIGHTIE WITH LACE TRIM 3.00

J 25-455-3 GARNET VELVET COAT AND MATCHING HAT 6.95

J 25-455-4 GREEN VELVET COAT AND MATCHING HAT 6.95

K 25-36 DOTTED ORGANDY TORSO DRESS. BLUE 4.50

L 25-480 MINK STOLE, EVENING BAG, GLASSES, RING AND BRACELET 5.00

M 25-454-3 TAFFETA EVENING GOWN, RED 7.95

M 25-454-1 TAFFETA EVENING GOWN, ROSE 7.95

25-430 EVENING PETTICOAT (Not Illus.) 3.00

25-355-1 CAN-CAN PETTICOAT PINK (Not Illus.) 2.75

25-250 LACE CHEMISE (Not Illus.) 3.00

25-32 BERMUDA BEACH SET (white beach robe, blue shorts and halter), not illus. 4.50

28

B DOLL This demure miss in a brand new size. She ister, 11½" tall, her sweet beautifully by her saran can walk, sit or kneel as her legs are jointed at the knee and her arms at the elbow. She poses gracefully in most any position. Made entirely of hard plastic, her eyes open and close.

A 26-86 LISSY IN SCHOOL DRESS 10.00
Solid red polished cotton dress with crisp white organdy collar, cuffs and pinafore with red feather stitching. Lace trimmed taffeta petticoat. Ship. wt. 3 lbs.

B 26-96 LISSY IN PROM DRESS 10.95
She's the belle of the ball in her gown of sheer nylon tulle with bodice of silver dotted net and satin sash, tulle and rosebud headdress, flowered nosegay, strap sandals with baby Louis heels and nylon stockings. Ship. wt. 3 lbs.

C 26-85 LISSY IN COAT AND HAT 10.00
Fully lined blue and white checked coat covers a simple taffeta dress. Straw hat trimmed with berries, strap sandals and white socks. Ship. wt. 3 lbs.

D 25-90 FLOWERED NYLON ROBE, pink 2.00

E 25-92 SILK NIGHTIE, pink 2.00

F 25-83 PLEATED NET DANCE FROCK, lace bodice 5.95

G 25-84 NET BALLET TOU-TOU, satin bodice, pink 4.50

H 25-81 POLISHED COTTON PINAFORE DRESS 4.00

J 25-89 3 PIECE SPORT OUTFIT, checked skirt, organdy blouse 4.75

K 25-94 GABARDINE COAT, blue with red velvet poke hat 4.75

L 16-81 DOLL'S CLOTHES RACK (Exclusive)
Ship. wt. 2 lbs. 3.95
A well made wooden clothes rack suitable for dolls 11" to 20", to help keep their clothes in neat array. The base of the rack is a full length drawer for dolly's shoes, socks, slips, panties, etc., while the top shelf is for her hats. Clothes, etc., are not included.

M 40-169 CISSY TAKES A TRIP (From our Studio) 55.00
Off on one of her frequent cruises, Cissy the Debutante Doll (as described on opposite page) enjoys a trousseau that is both smart and practical. Packed within the roomy 24" trunk (as described on page 33) is a stunning full skirted evening gown of lace-trimmed blue net over a lace-trimmed taffeta underskirt and an organdy hooped petticoat. Form fitting bodice of delicate blue taffeta with net-trimmed neckline and a flower on each shoulder. For daytime wear, Cissy has a red print cotton full skirted sundress with white ric-rac trim and large matching bow, tasteful and chic. At night, she wears a lace-trimmed silk nightie and a glamourous flowered nylon negligee. The "Bon Voyage" outfit that she is wearing, a taffeta lined black and white flared skirt over a red can-can petticoat, white pique blouse with Peter Pan collar, and matching bolero jacket. White straw hat, black high-heel sandals and nylon stockings complete her eye-catching costume. Accessories included for Cissy's trip are silver evening slippers, flowered mules, nylon stockings, handbag, gloves, sunglasses, comb, brush and mirror. Ship. wt. 20 lbs. Express.

N 26-98 LISSY AND HER WARDROBE 15.95
Lissy, as described above, dressed in a dainty chemise of Swiss eyelet embroidery, strap sandals and socks. Her 9 piece wardrobe provides the proper clothing for any hour of the day. Silk nightie, nylon robe, coat and hat, taffeta dress, petticoat, panties, curlers, shoes and a plastic barette. Packed in attractive box with clear plastic window. Ship. wt. 3 lbs.

FREE DELIVERY
TO 13 EASTERN STATES
SEE INSIDE BACK COVER

29

Cissy was a hit for F.A.O. Schwarz and she was given a full page in the 1956 Christmas catalog.

Below: In addition to dressed dolls and boxed fashions, a trunk set called Cissy Takes a Trip was made exclusively for F.A.O. Schwarz. The set sold for $55 and included a doll dressed in a skirt, blouse and jacket plus a ball gown, nightgown, robe, sundress and various accessories all inside a large metal trunk.

Another part of the allure of F.A.O. Schwarz to Madame Alexander was the high visibility that Cissy received in the flagship New York City store. Since the dolls and clothing were expensive, AND a new concept in the mid-1950s, product visibility in a prestigious setting was considered crucial by Madame Alexander. Many of Madame Alexander's smaller accounts did not have the resources or the space to display and market the large 21" Cissy doll. At F.A.O., Cissy would always be in the spotlight, usually behind glass and surrounded by other exclusive items such as furniture and chaise lounges not made by the Alexander Doll Company, but part of a brilliant strategy to market Cissy and tie her into other exclusive products.

It was this exposure, in the high-end world of F.A.O. Schwarz, that Cissy would become the darling of the new genre of high heeled, full figure dolls, a title that she maintains today among her many fans. It was easy to see why

A 25-508 LISSY THE SUB DEB DOLL 5.00
This demure Miss is sophisticated Cissy's younger sister. 11½" tall, her sweet young face set off beautifully by her saran hair. Lissy can walk, sit or kneel, as her legs are jointed at the knee and her arms at the elbow. Made entirely of hard plastic, her eyes open and close. Dressed in a prim taffeta chemise with lace ruffle, as well as nylon stockings and strap slippers. Ship. wt. 3 lbs.

B 25-359 DOTTED BLUE COTTON RESORT DRESS with white pique trim and full petticoat............ 3.50

C 25-360 ORGANDY PARTY DRESS with matching hat and taffeta petticoat............ 5.00

D 25-361 SILK NIGHTIE............ 1.50

E 25-362 BEACH OUTFIT............ 3.50
Green flowered challis robe lined with terry cloth and matching bathing suit.

F 25-363 RUFFLED NYLON FANCY SLIP............ 2.00

G 25-364 FLOWERED NYLON ROBE.. 2.00

25-365 ALL WEATHER COAT AND HAT (Not Illus.) Fine red and white check............ 3.00

H 26-3 CISSY THE DEBUTANTE DOLL 16.95
A 20" young lady with a slim delicately molded figure and beautifully shaped feet that wear only high-heeled shoes. Her head, body and jointed legs are of hard, high-quality plastic, while her jointed arms are of soft plastic. Cissy's head can be posed in life-like positions and she can walk. Her fashionable saran coiffure further accentuates her "grown-up" look. Dressed in afternoon dress of yellow and violet cotton print with an organdy can-can petticoat, lace-trimmed undies and flower bedecked straw hat. Ship. wt. 7 lbs.

26-20 CISSY IN CHEMISE (Not Illus.) 12.95

J 25-11 FANCY STRAW HAT WITH FLOWER SPRAY............ 2.50

K 25-12 SPRING COAT Pink, taffeta lined with Peter Pan Collar....... 4.50

L 25-13 AFTERNOON FROCK checked nylon with lace trim............ 4.50

M 25-14 RUFFLED TAFFETA CAN-CAN PETTICOAT............ 2.50

N 25-15 3-PIECE SPORTS OUTFIT...... 4.50
Pleated skirt, shorts and blouse, all of striped cotton.

P 25-16 LACE TRIMMED COTTON NIGHTIE WITH RIBBON SASH.......... 3.50

R 25-17 BLUE AND WHITE POLKA DOT PIQUE ROBE............ 3.50

25-18 BATHING SUIT WITH STRAW SUN HAT (Not Illus.)............ 3.00

S 26-272 POOR PITIFUL PEARL........ 10.00
This pathetic little tyke needs a young mother to give her loving care and affection. A cartoon character created by Steig. Poor Pitiful Pearl is 18" tall, of all vinyl and has long washable saran wig that needs a "mother's" attention. She arrives with a complete change of clothing that transforms her into a sparkling little party girl. In carrying case. 4 lbs.

T 25-528 DOLL'S CLOTHES RACK...... 3.00
An exclusive well made 4 x 9½ x 10½" wooden clothes rack to help keep dolly's clothes in neat array. The base of the rack is a full length chest for shoes, socks, slips, panties, etc., while the top shelf is for hats. Mahogany finish. Wt. 2 lbs.

W 12-15 WARDROBE wt. 6 lbs....... 5.00
7 x 4½ x 10½". Hanger rod, hat shelf. Clothes not included. Mahogany finish.

X 12-21 COLONIAL BED wt. 5 lbs..... 5.95
7½ x 11¼ x 11½" high. Turned corner posts, curved tester. With dotted Swiss canopy cover, spread and bolster, with ruffled edges, and mattress. Mahogany finish.

29

Cissy was again shown in the 1957 summer catalog with a doll and several fashions.

Madame Alexander would be attracted to a store that prided itself in offering unique products in an unforgettable environment.

In 1990, Cissy by Scassi was introduced as an exclusive for F.A.O. This was the first new Cissy doll in almost 30 years! While the costume, designed by fashion designer Arnold Scassi was stunning, and the doll was lovely, the timing just didn't seem to be right, as small fashion dolls were still the mainstay of the doll world and she lacked that sparkle for which Cissy was known.

Today, Cissy has been widely accepted and once again graces the floor to ceiling showcase windows of F.A.O. Schwarz where collectors and fans and even the casual tourist from around the globe can see her in all her finery. F.A.O. Schwarz, considered to be the leading specialty retailer of toys and collectibles in the United States, and Madame Alexander, the grand dame of dolls, is a match made in heaven!

F.A.O. SCHWARZ
FIFTH AVENUE AT 58TH STREET

Madame Alexander Dolls

CISSY, THE DEBUTANTE DOLL Not a baby doll, but a 20" young lady with a slim, delicately molded figure and beautifully shaped feet that wear only high-heeled shoes. Her head, body and jointed legs are of hard, high-quality plastic, while her jointed arms are of soft plastic. Cissy's head can be posed in life-like positions and she can walk. Her beautiful saran coiffure further accentuates her "grown-up" look.

A 16-37 CISSY AS QUEEN ELIZABETH Wt. 7 lbs. **25.00**
Court gown of gold brocade, worn over taffeta hoop petticoat with Order of the Garter with star, long white gloves and tiara, earrings and bracelets jeweled with rhinestones.

B 26-72 CISSY IN EVENING GOWN Ship. wt. 7 lbs. **25.00**
Elegantly gowned for the opera in an unusual blue and white lace print creation with sweeping circular skirt. Velvet sash is caught at the waistline with a corsage of roses. Satin lined cape stole of orlon ermine included.

C 16-30 CISSY IN GARDEN PARTY DRESS **22.95**
A large flower trimmed picture hat matches her charming nylon net dress, worn over a blush pink taffeta petticoat. Accessories include a wide satin sash, earrings, necklace and ring. Ship. wt. 7 lbs.

D 26-29 CISSY IN TEATIME DRESS Wt. 5 lbs. **17.95**
Stylish pink and white checked lace-trimmed nylon dress worn over taffeta can-can petticoat that rustles when she walks. Smart flower-trimmed straw hat completes her costume.

E 16-34 CISSY IN AFTERNOON DRESS Wt. 5 lbs. **20.00**
Ready to "step Out" in this smart blue velvet jumper with pink silk blouse over lace-trimmed petticoat. Fashionable pendant watch hangs from her waist. Matching straw hat with pink flowered trim.

F 26-20 CISSY IN UNDIES Ship. wt. 5 lbs. **12.95**
In lace chemise, stockings and flowered mules. NEGLIGEE NOT INCLUDED. See below.

25-31 LACE-TRIMMED NYLON NEGLIGEE **3.50**
(As illus. on Cissy)

G 25-45 STOLE AND JEWELRY ACCESSORY KIT **4.50**
Including gold slippers, nylon stockings, sunglasses, handbag and hankie.

H 25-44 EVENING DRESS **8.95**
Blue and white lace print, with taffeta petticoat.

J 25-27 COTTON PRINT TORSO DRESS **4.00**

K 25-24 PINK CREPE NIGHTIE **3.50**
25-22 LACE CHEMISE (Not Illus.) **3.00**
25-23 CORSELET (Not Illus.) **3.00**
25-39 LACE PETTICOAT AND PANTIES (Not Illus.) **2.50**

L 25-38 IMITATION FUR COAT, with hood and muff **8.95**

25-18 BATHING SUIT with hat (not illustrated) **3.00**

M 25-36 VELVET TOREADOR PANTS, with lace blouse **5.00**

25-46 FELT COAT AND HAT, beige with scarf (not illus.) **4.50**

28

The 1957 Christmas catalog featured a full page of Cissy dolls, fashions, and accessories.

In the 1958 Christmas catalog, Cissy no longer received top billing in the Madame Alexander section. She was selling so well, she didn't need the exposure. There are two dressed dolls and many individual fashions and accessories shown in this catalog.

A KATHY BABY Sweet-faced little charmer, made entirely of soft molded vinyl and fully jointed for versatile play. Kathy has rooted Saran hair, goes to sleep, cries real tears, has a voice, drinks and wets. She is dressed in lace-trimmed organdy with frothy bonnet of dotted nylon ruffles. Satin baby shoes complete her costume.

26-17	15" tall. Ship. wt. 3 lbs.	10.95
26-21	18" tall. Ship. wt. 4 lbs.	13.95
26-99	21" tall. Ship. wt. 7 lbs.	18.95

CISSY, THE DEBUTANTE DOLL A 20" young lady with a slim, delicately molded figure and beautifully shaped feet that wear only high-heeled shoes. Her head, body and jointed legs are of hard, high-quality plastic, while her jointed arms are of soft plastic. Cissy's head can be posed in life-like positions and she can walk. Her beautiful saran coiffure further accentuates her grown-up look.

B 26-119 CISSY IN GARDEN PARTY DRESS 25.00
A large rose-trimmed lace-straw picture hat matches her dainty flowery net dress, with full skirt cascading from the fitted bodice. Fingertip gloves and jewels complete her costume. Ship. wt. 7 lbs.

C 26-120 CISSY IN EVENING GOWN Wt. 7 lbs. **25.00**
Cissy is radiant in her elegant gown of soft white silk, with pink camellias in a wide spaced print. Her long rose velvet cape stole is lined to match her gown. Her gold veil, caught up with flowers, and her tasteful jewelry are sure to make her "coming out" a success.

CLOTHES FOR CISSY—Ship. wt. 1 lb. each

D	**25-2**	**FLANNEL COAT AND HAT**	**6.95**
E	**16-46-3**	**RED DINNER DRESS WITH PETTICOAT**	**8.95**
F	**25-30**	**RED AND BLACK SPORT OUTFIT**	**4.50**
G	**25-47**	**NAUTICAL OUTFIT**	**5.00**
H	**25-25**	**PINK CREPE ROBE**	**3.50**
J	**25-24**	**PINK CREPE NIGHTIE**	**3.50**
K	**25-43**	**JEWELRY AND STOLE SET**	**4.50**
	25-7	**PETTICOAT AND PANTIES** (Not Illus.)	**2.50**
	25-37	**CHEMISE** (Not Illus.)	**3.00**
	25-13	**TOREADOR OUTFIT** (Not Illus.)	**5.00**

L 26-118 SHIRLEY TEMPLE DOLL Wt. 6 lbs. **15.00**
Movie viewers of the 30's have never forgotten Shirley Temple, the golden-headed moppet with the dimpled smile and flirting eyes. And the recent revival of those films on television has expanded her popularity to today's youngsters. This 19" version of Shirley has those same mischievous eyes, rooted blonde curls, soft vinyl head, hard vinyl arms and legs and that famous smile. She wears a dainty lace-trimmed pink or blue nylon party dress, shoes and socks. STATE COLOR.

M 12-23 CISSETTE TRAVEL TROUSSEAU 21.75
(Exclusive) Smart, sophisticated Cissette (a 9½" version of her glamorous big sister) is every inch a debutante. Ensconced in her trim 12" fibreboard case, Cissette's molded figure is set off effectively by a chic assortment of clothing including pink polished cotton afternoon dress with full skirt, lace-trimmed undies and straw hat. On individual hangers in the wardrobe portion of the case are silk nightie and robe, blue street dress with slip and panties, a red and white sport slack set and a pair of mules. Ship. wt. 5 lbs.

N KATHY CHRISTENING DOLLS The same lovable Kathy as described in "A" above, here dressed in a long white Christening dress of imported organdy with narrow ruffles of val lace. Her dainty bonnet has double lace frills.

26-54 KATHY	11". Ship. wt. 2 lbs.	**7.95**
26-24 KATHY	15". Ship. wt. 4 lbs.	**12.95**

FREE DELIVERY TO 13 EASTERN STATES SEE INSIDE BACK COVER

30

ps, panties, etc., while the top shelf

M 40-209 CISSY TAKES A TRIP (exclusive) **55.00**
Off on one of her frequent cruises, Cissy enjoys a trousseau that is both smart and practical. Packed within the roomy 24" trunk is a stunning full skirted evening gown with underskirt and hooped petticoat. For daytime wear, Cissy has a print cotton full skirted sundress with ric-rac trim tasteful and chic. For sportswear, she has colorful slacks with white nylon lace-trimmed blouse. At night she wears a lace-trimmed silk nightie and a glamourous flowered nylon negligee. The "Bon Voyage" outfit that she is wearing is a full-flared skirt with striped cotton tailored blouse and chatelaine watch. Coche hat, high-heel sandals and nylon stockings complete her eye-catching costume. Accessories included are gold evening slippers, flowered mules, nylon stockings, flower-trimmed fan, handbag, sunglasses, comb, brush and mirror. Ship. wt. 20 lbs. EXPRESS.

29

The exclusive Cissy trunk for 1957 was again called Cissy Takes a Trip. While the price for the set remained at $55, the set had more clothing than the 1956 trunk.

p. wt. 9 lbs. 16.75
into this charming white
it gently to sleep as the
une. Lace-trimmed pillow,
white print dimity cover,
ade especially for the 22"
OT INCLUDED. See below.
Ship. wt. 3 lbs. 7.95
dress. Drinks and wets.
8 lbs. 8.75
oll's life as a bed or a
wooden 19 x 19 x 12"
oard floor. Natural wood
CLUDED. See below.
wt. 5 lbs. 10.00
ed plastic. Fully jointed,
has a voice. Dressed in
bonnet.
14 lbs. Express only 18.00
an be in this 30 x 15"
and sturdy wood slats.
red with pink percale.
ite dimity with red polka
d ruffles on the spread.
hip. wt. 8 lbs. 6.00
y "little mother" knows
wooden chair, 28" high,
ombination of red plastic
ble tray and foot rest.
D 26.95
d roomy enough (20½"
eep the largest or several
upport the arched canopy
risp white ruffled duster.
hogany finish. With mat-
Express
ip. wt. 10 lbs. 18.00
wide, 22" high.
hip. wt. 5 lbs. 8.00
½" wide 14¾" high.

F 44-28 BUNK BED Ship. wt. 22 lbs. Express. 26.95
Here is the ideal space-saving double decker bed, in maple finish with fancy turned wooden posts and maple ladder. The dainty pink dotted Swiss spreads with matching ruffles are lined with pink percale. Mattresses and pillows included. Approximate measurement is 29 x 14 x 27" DOLL NOT INCLUDED. See below.

26-25 CISSY DOLL—20" tall in undies and nylon robe. Wt. 7 lbs. 16.50

20-33 SINGLE BED (Not Illustrated) Ship. wt. 11 lbs. 13.95
Certainly the most fastidious doll would be pleased by the hardwood frame in maple finish with fancy turned wooden p... and lovely red-figured white percale spread with ruffles trimmed w... Approximate size: 13 x 1... tress and pillow included.

G 25-528 DOLL'S CLOTHES RACK Mahogany fini...
An exclusive well made 4 x 9½ x 10½" wooden... keep dolly's clothes in neat array. The base of the... chest for shoes, socks, slips, panties, etc., while th... Mahogany finish.

H 12-15 WARDROBE (Mahogany Finish) Ship. ...
7 x 4½ x 10½. Hanger rod, hat shelf. Clothes not ...

J 12-11 COLONIAL BED Mahogany finish. wt. 5...
8½ x 13½ x 12" high. Turned corner posts, cur... Swiss canopy cover, spread and bolster, with ...

A Cissy dress in a nylon robe with panties was shown climbing into a bunk bed in the F.A.O. Schwarz catalogs from 1957-1960. Cissy's main purpose was to market the wooden bed.

CISSY, THE DEBUTANTE DOLL — A 20" young lady with a slim, delicately molded figure and beautifully shaped feet that wear only high-heeled shoes. Her head, body and jointed legs are of hard, high-quality plastic, while her jointed arms are of soft plastic. Cissy's head can be posed in life-like positions and she can walk. Her beautiful saran coiffure further accentuates her grown-up look.

A 26-99 CISSY IN GAY NINETIES DRESS Ship. wt. 7 lbs. 26.95
A long bouffant skirt of pink taffeta, set off by her fitted velvet jacket of orchid elaborately trimmed with embroidery and silk braid. Matching flower-trimmed straw hat with a cloud of soft veiling. Earrings and ring complete her costume.

B 16-28 CISSY AS QUEEN ELIZABETH Ship. wt. 7 lbs. 25.00
Court gown of white brocade, worn over taffeta hoop petticoat with Order of the Garter with star, long white gloves and tiara, earrings, ring, and jewelled bracelets.

CLOTHES FOR CISSY—Ship. wt. 1 lb. each

C	25-4	Lace Robe	4.00
D	25-36	Pink Crepe Nightie	4.00
E	25-38	Striped Skirt and Sweater	6.00
F	25-7	Petticoat and Panties	2.50
G	25-31-3	Red Evening Dress	8.95
H	25-28-1	Coral Wool Coat and Hat	8.00
	25-28-2	Royal Blue Wool Coat and Hat	8.00

J 26-118 SHIRLEY TEMPLE DOLL 15.00
Movie viewers of the 30's have never forgotten Shirley Temple, the golden-headed moppet with the dimpled smile and flirting eyes. And the recent revival of those films on television has expanded her popularity to today's youngsters. This 19" version of Shirley has those same mischievous eyes, rooted blonde curls, soft vinyl head, hard vinyl arms and legs and that famous smile. She wears a pink or blue dress with dainty lace-trimmed white nylon pinafore, shoes and socks. STATE COLOR. Ship. wt. 6 lbs.

K CHRISTENING DOLL—The same lovable Kathy as described in "N" on this page, here dressed in a long white Christening dress of imported lace-trimmed organdy. She also wears a long organdy coat with matching bonnet.
26-59 KATHY 11" Ship. wt. 2 lbs. 10.00

L-M KATHLEEN TODDLER — Looking just like anyone's favorite chubby little girl, 23" Kathleen has an all vinyl body, rooted hair and roving eyes. She drinks and wets and has movable arms, legs and head. Her dimpled hands and knees add to her little girl charm. Ship. wt. 7 lbs. each.

L 16-16 KATHLEEN TODDLER 15.95
Wearing polished cotton polka dot dress with lace-trimmed collar and cuffs. Pink or Blue. STATE COLOR.

M 16-17 KATHLEEN TODDLER 18.00
Wearing lace-trimmed nylon party dress with matching poke bonnet. Pink or Blue. STATE COLOR.

N KATHY BABY—Sweet-faced little charmer, made entirely of soft molded vinyl and fully jointed for versatile play. Kathy has rooted Saran hair, goes to sleep, cries real tears, has a voice, drinks and wets. She is dressed in pink lace-trimmed pleated nylon with frothy bonnet of nylon ruffles. Satin baby shoes complete her costume.

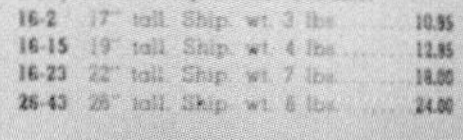

16-2	17" tall. Ship. wt. 3 lbs.	10.95
16-15	19" tall. Ship. wt. 4 lbs.	12.95
16-23	22" tall. Ship. wt. 7 lbs.	18.00
26-43	26" tall. Ship. wt. 6 lbs.	24.00

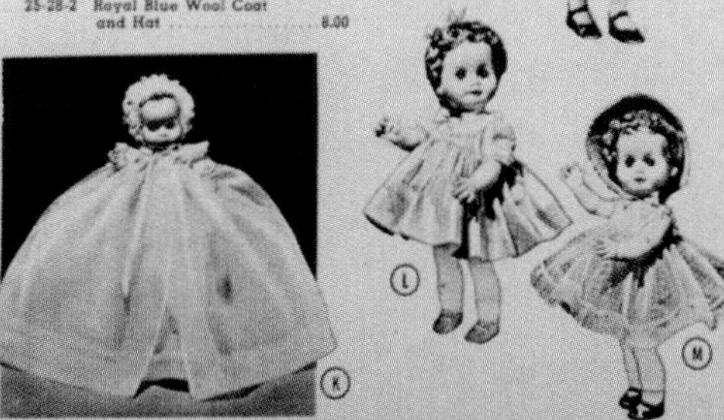

30

The 1959 Christmas catalog again has two Cissy dolls and various outfits. What is most interesting is that there is a "Cissy in a Gay Nineties Dress" featured which is actually the Godey Portrait Cissy from 1961. Based on this information, it is possible that the doll was produced earlier for F.A.O. Schwarz than the other retailers.

There's Something Extra About A Schwarz Exclusive!

A 40-99 ROYAL TOUR TROUSSEAU 75.00
A beautiful 20" young queen, regal in appearance, with slim delicately molded figure, and jointed arms and legs. She can be posed in life-like positions, walk, or sit, and does them all gracefully. She wears her court gown of gold brocade over a taffeta hoop petticoat, with Order of the Garder, long white gloves, tiara, earrings, ring and jewelled bracelets. Packed into the 24" metal-covered trunk with her is a large trousseau that includes afternoon tea dress, print dress, cloak, sports slacks, silk nightie and robe, chemise, shoes, mules, stockings and accessories. Express Only. Ship. wt. 22 lbs.

B 12-31 CAT FAMILY (Import) **24.50**
Solemn, affectionate, quizzical, playful, tired, asleep. Each a furry plush masterpiece of the world famous Steiff workshop, this lovable family of felix domesticus expresses all of these typically catlike states of mind. Comfortable on a soft 24" x 13" red cushion is the proud mother tiger cat surrounded by her four offspring, all of whom are feeling deeply the joy of good living. The small gray mouse sitting undisturbed in a corner attests to the good nature of the kittens. Wt. 5 lbs.

When we say "exclusive, unique", we mean just that. The toys on this page are only here, here in the Schwarz wonderland of playthings where toys are a way of life.

But the adjectives that really count are the squeals of delight, the shining eyes, the fun-filled hours, and the fond memories of a favorite toy that, happily, can last a lifetime.

C 60-48 GARAGE (Import) **50.00**
Twelve friction-powered cars and trucks ...

JACQUELINE AT THE BALL—A beautiful 20" debutante, Jacqueline is a designer's delight. Her jointed arms and legs allow her to sit gracefully and pose in other lifelike positions. Her dark saran hair is arranged in a fashionable coiffure, and her dark lashes add to her loveliness. Made of hard plastic with a beautifully molded figure that enhances her elegance. Ship. wt. 5 lbs. each.

A 826-3 JACQUELINE IN BALL GOWN 25.00
Full-length, lined evening coat of crimson satin over elegant white brocade ball gown.

B 816-60 JACQUELINE IN EVENING SUIT 23.00
Stunning full-length evening suit of white brocade.

C 826-7 QUEEN ELIZABETH DOLL Ship. wt. 5 lbs. **25.00**
Every inch a Queen, this regal 20" doll, fully jointed in arms and legs for an ever-graceful posture, is dressed in a court gown of brocade, decorated with the sash of the Order of the Bath. Features of the doll same as Jacqueline described above. She wears a brilliant tiara on her shining light hair. Long white gloves and "jewels" fit for a Queen included.

CLOTHES FOR JACQUELINE AND QUEEN

D 825-71 WHITE BROCADE FORMAL GOWN 10.95
Exquisitely fashioned with flaring side panels of rose satin.

E 825-57 SPORT SKIRT AND JERSEY 3.00
F 825-58 WHITE LEATHERETTE JACKET AND HAT 4.00
G 825-63 PINK LACE-TRIMMED NIGHTIE 4.00
H 825-65 MATCHING ROBE 4.00
J 825-67 BLUE WOOL SUIT AND MATCHING HAT 8.00
K 816-23 ELISE BALLERINA 14.00
The sweetness of Elise's pretty face is matched by the grace of her body, with its jointed arms, legs, knees and ankles. She sits and poses naturally, and can wear high or low heels. 16" tall, Elise has saran hair, a hard plastic head and body, and soft vinyl arms. She wears a tou-tou of pink nylon tulle with a bodice of sequins that matches her coronet. Ship. wt. 3 lbs.

L-M SWEETIE WALKER—A 23" towhead toddler with light saran hair tied with a ribbon bow. When led by the hand, Sweetie toddles along, gazing in wide-eyed wonder at the world about her. Her head, arms, and legs are jointed. Her body and legs are of hard plastic, her head and arms of soft vinyl. Ship. wt. 6 lbs. each.

L 816-12 SWEETIE WALKER IN PLAY DRESS 12.95
Ruffled, rose-print dress with puffed sleeves of organdy and matching bloomer.

M 816-13 SWEETIE WALKER IN SUNDAY BEST 16.95
Polished pique coat over dotted Swiss dress.

"BUNNY" DOLL—A newcomer to our family of dolls is darling little Bunny. Her sweet smile and childlike postures add much to that irresistible little girl charm. Fully jointed and made of lightweight, durable plastic, Bunny has shining saran hair. Her big eyes go to sleep at bedtime. 18" tall. Ship. wt. 3 lbs.

N 826-1 BUNNY IN PARTY DRESS 10.00
Dress of dotted Swiss, trimmed with organdy ruffle and Peter Pan collar.

P 816-10 BUNNY IN SUNDAY BEST 12.95
Pique coat with matching bonnet over white pique dress.

CLOTHES FOR BUNNY (Illustrated)

R 825-177 FLOWERED NYLON NIGHTIE 2.50
S 825-180 MATCHING ROBE 3.50
T 825-178 PIQUE DRESS AND BLOOMER 3.00
U 825-181 COTTON DRESS AND BLOOMER 3.50
V 825-182 ROSE PIQUE COAT AND BONNET 5.00

CLOTHES FOR SWEETIE WALKER

825-115 FLOWERED NYLON NIGHTIE (illus. "R") **3.50**
825-116 MATCHING ROBE (illus. "S") **4.00**
825-118 FLOWERED COTTON DRESS AND BLOOMER, shown on Doll "L" **3.50**
825-119 DOTTED SWISS DRESS AND BLOOMER, not illus. **4.50**
825-117 POLISHED PIQUE COAT, as shown on Doll "M" **5.00**

42

Above: Aside from Cissy with the bunk bed, the only Cissy item featured in the 1960 F.A.O. Schwarz Christmas catalog was an exclusive trunk set called the Royal Tour Trousseau. The trunk set sold for $75 and included a Cissy Queen doll in a gold brocade gown plus several other fashions and accessories.

The only other Cissy shown in the F.A.O. Schwarz Christmas catalogs from 1961 until her retirement in 1963, was the Cissy Queen and that was in the 1962 catalog. The name Cissy was not used and the doll was called Queen Elizabeth.

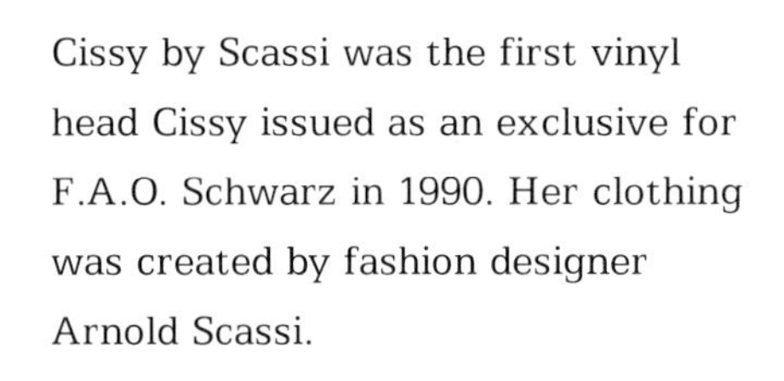

Cissy by Scassi was the first vinyl head Cissy issued as an exclusive for F.A.O. Schwarz in 1990. Her clothing was created by fashion designer Arnold Scassi.

Layer of tulle accented with sequins, the doll was pretty, but the public wasn't ready for Cissy just yet.

Yardley products for America are created in England, and finished in the U.S.A. from the original English formulas, combining imported and domestic ingredients. Yardley of London, Inc., 620 Fifth Ave., N.Y.C.

To make you feel especially feminine
YARDLEY fragrances ... of course

Which of these lovely, lingering scents is for you? The vibrant sophistication of Bond Street? Delicately exotic Lotus? Perhaps it's April Violets, rain-sweet and incurably romantic. Or is your one and only love the fresh, lighthearted gaiety of Lavender? Not an easy choice to make—but a delightful one. These toilet waters and colognes from $1.25 plus tax.

Chapter 9

Cissy and Yardley

Yardley of London...a name that sparks magic and has since 1770 is back! Actually, the now well-known name was first recognized 150 years earlier during the reign of King Charles I, when a young man named Yardley paid the king a great sum of money to become the "official" soap maker to the city of London and the royal family. As with others, the "official to the royal family" stamp of approval whose names include Louis Vuitton, today means that the business is the only one that the British royals use throughout the empire. The particulars of this transaction were lost in the great fire of London in 1666, but the contract was saved with Yardley and the legacy lives on.

Lavender is a fragrance known to London and Yardley based a business on just that fragrance with a touch of English Rose and Narcissus. The company has always been known for a unique floral scent.

Always considered a high end product, Yardley of London entered into a licensing agreement with the Alexander Doll Company in the mid-1950s to produce ads for women's magazines. Actually, it was an agreement desperately needed by both companies. Yardley of London needed to be established in the United States in order to increase sales and the Alexander Doll Company wanted the Cissy doll tied into something traditional to offset her "adult" image as a children's toy for the upper classes.

The campaign was a success, as many ads appeared featuring the Cissy doll with unique hairstyles and clothing. Today, the Alexander Doll Company is reproducing the dolls and accessories used in these 1950s ads. Even those who could not afford the Cissy doll now know that such a doll existed, which was the goal of the campaign for the Alexander Doll Company. Tradition was highly valued in the 1950s, after decades of turmoil.

Even after the Cissy doll was discontinued, Yardley of London still maintained a connection to United States shoppers. In 1967, they entered into an exclusive agreement with Twiggy, the Mod model, to market eye make-up based on the look that Twiggy had brought to the United States.

Opposite page: One of the most common ads is this Cissy with a deck of playing cards.

Today Yardley is eagerly embracing its relationship once again with the Alexander Doll Company and the current issues of "Yardley Cissy" dolls are among the most sought after of the Cissy doll line.

The return of traditional old-fashioned marketing techniques is refreshing in our current techno age. The so-called Yardley Cissy dolls are destined to be the collectibles of the future. Meanwhile, Yardley continues to entice American consumers with its new line of Lavender Inspirations. With a new line featuring a Ginger and Lime fragrance and with the new Yardley inspired Cissy dolls, one can only see a tradition that dates back almost 50 years come alive once again!

While the Cissy with playing cards is the most common ad, locating one in this half page vertical format is more challenging.

Opposite page: An interesting black and white version of the ad. Not only is Yardley promoting their products, but it is also an ad for the *Ladies' Home Journal* magazine.

Yardley has two favorite salesladies

John F. Bales, Vice-President in Charge of Sales for Yardley of London, never underestimates the power of a woman!

Surprisingly, Yardley's two favorite salesladies are not real people. Yet both have created very real results on Yardley's sales charts.

One is a Yardley doll…the other is the No. 1 women's magazine, Ladies' Home Journal.

The doll has been selling Yardley cosmetics for only about a year—but Yardley reports that she has been doing more of a job than any real-live girl. For she symbolizes everything that's fresh and feminine.

The Journal has been selling Yardley cosmetics for nearly 35 years. And here's what Yardley says about the Journal: "This year, as in the past, Ladies' Home Journal spearheads our list of media. The Journal reflects beauty from cover to cover—but that's not all. Women seem to feel a special way about the Journal. The relationship between women and the magazine is intimate and personal. This is a perfect climate for sales."

Thanks to these two salesladies, Yardley continues to maintain an impressive sales pattern that is stronger than ever!

Never underestimate the power of the No. 1 magazine for women…

Ladies' Home JOURNAL

A CURTIS PUBLICATION

No. 1 in circulation
No. 1 in newsstand sales
No. 1 in advertising revenue

Above: These two ads are smaller in size and appeared in *Reader's Digest* magazine.

Another common Yardley ad.

The harder-to-find half page vertical format.

From *Glamour* magazine, a black and white version, also more difficult to locate.

Right: Another ad, only this time in German. Yardley and Cissy became globally recognized with this ad campaign. *From the collection of Laura Colpus.*

Cissy plays the violin in this Yardley ad.

This Cissy doll is wearing a reproduction of the "violin" dress. The Alexander Doll Company began a series of Yardley dolls in 2000. This doll was the first in the series and was limited to 750 dolls.

The violin ad in the hard-to-find vertical format. Notice the additional products featured in this ad.

Below: The harder-to-find black and white version.

The chair is so typical of the 1950s furniture. The Alexander Doll Company reproduced the doll and chair for collectors in 2002, and called her Sitting Pretty Cissy.

The doll in this soap ad was given the name Morning Ritual Cissy when the Alexander Doll Company produced her in 2001.

Another easy-to-locate ad, is this soap ad.

Below: The same ad in the smaller size from *Reader's Digest* magazine. Note the ad on the left is written in French and came from a Canadian *Reader's Digest*.

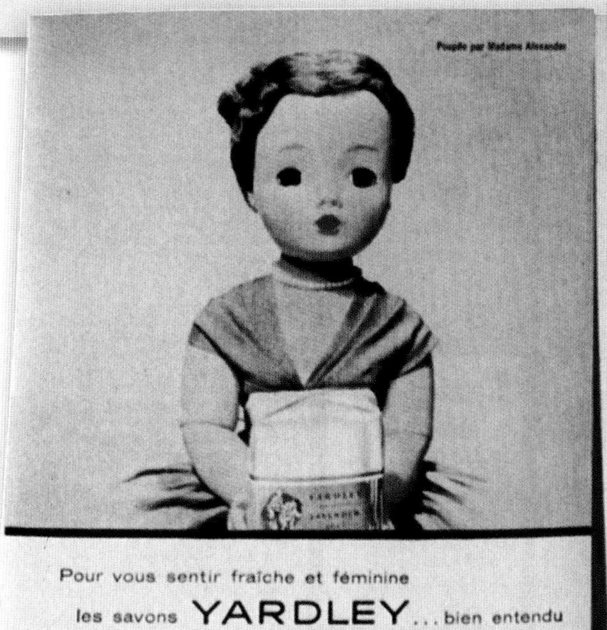

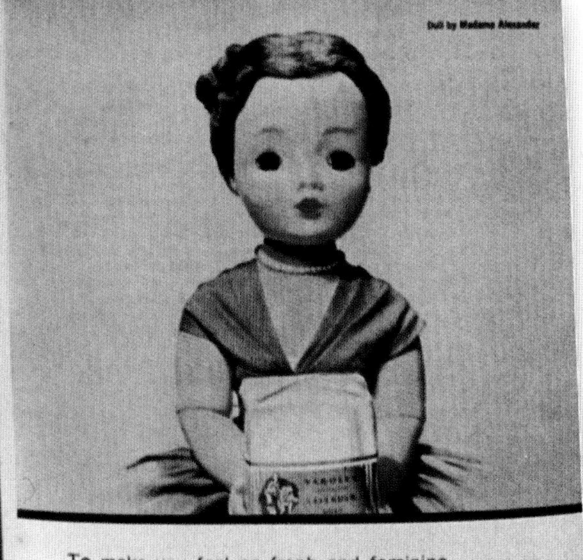

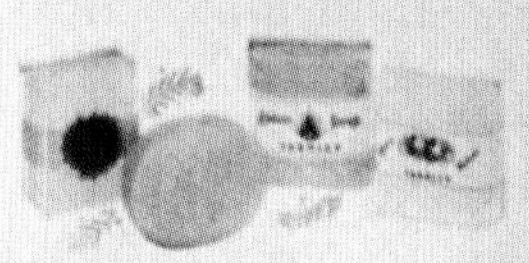

This ad for dusting powder is relatively easy to locate.

Another ad for dusting powder, but this one is more difficult to locate.

This gingham dress ad is hard to locate.

The vertical format is even more difficult to find.

The "Flair" ad features Cissy ready for an evening out. A difficult ad to locate.

The "tiara" ad featuring the Bond Street Perfume was only done in black and white and is hard to find.

Another hard-to-find Bond Street black and white ad.

A favorite of many collectors is this ad featuring Cissy in a chic evening suit. This ad is also hard to find.

Price Guide

When buying a doll, the first thing is to set a budget. Know how much you can spend on your collection. Next, decide if you want fewer dolls and better quality or more dolls with less quality. The better the quality, the higher the price. Decide what you want to collect, will there be a central theme to your collection? For example, a person may decide to collect only ball gowns. Always ask the seller questions about the condition of the doll and their return policy should you be unhappy with your purchase. But the best advice is that you should buy what you like. It is your collection and you should enjoy it.

Condition and originality are the most important assets when buying a doll. These are the commonly used terms used in doll collecting to describe condition.

NRFB - Never Removed from Box, pristine, perfect and still in its original box, completely untouched.

Mint - The item is perfect. It looks like it was just made yesterday. A doll should be completely original with all body parts with no cracks, good facial and skin coloring, perfect hair. Clothing should be crisp and clean.

Near Mint or Excellent - The item displays beautifully. It's all original but it's lacking those qualities that make an item mint.

Very Good or Good - The item is all original. It may need some cleaning but should not be missing any important accessories. A doll should not have cut or missing hair.

Fair - The item has some problems. A doll may be pale, clothing may need mending. However, with a little work, these items can become part of a very nice collection.

Poor - Items that need major restoration or repair, although some items can be beyond repair. Don't forget to look at poor items, you never know when it might have something in good condition that you may need.

Complete - This means everything that originally came with the item is included.

Original - If it didn't come with the doll or fashion originally, it's not original.

HTF - Hard to find. Don't confuse this with rare. Rare is just that, an item that is hardly ever seen for sale, let alone in a collection. Hard to find is an item that doesn't come around often but is out there.

The pricing in this guide, is just that, a guide. Doll values change constantly based on supply and demand. Items that are hard to find will be priced higher than those items that are easily obtainable. The prices below are based on a Mint item (an item without a box and dolls without wrist tags) and any other condition should be priced accordingly.

Other Abbreviations Used Below:

CU - Collector's United

LE - Limited Edition

MADC - Madame Alexander Doll Club

UFDC - United Federation of Doll Clubs

Dressed Vintage Dolls	
Aqua Taffeta Dress with Ivory Satin Coat, #2021, 1956	$900
Basic Doll Wearing Chemise, Lingerie or Robe	$500
Black Taffeta Cocktail Dress with Lace, #2091, 1955	$900
Black Velvet Gown with Fur Stole, #2173, 1957	$1,000
Black Velvet Torso Gown, #2043, 1956	$900
Blue Satin Gown with Rhinestones, #2097, 1955	$1,500
Bride, 1955-1962	$1,000-$1,200
Bridesmaid, blue or pink, #2030, 1956	$1,000
Camellia Print Street Dress, pink or blue, #2222, 1958	$750
Cissy Walks Her Dog, 1956	$850
Forever Darling Bride, 1955	$3,000 up
Gainsborough Cissy, #2176, 1957	$1,200
Gardening Overalls and Blouse, 1957	$850
Godey Cissy	$1,500
Gold Lace Skirt with Jersey Blouse, #2115, 1959	$775

Gold Taffeta Gown with Matching Short Coat, #2098, 1955	$1,200
Heavy Faille Gown with Lace Overlay, #2172, 1957	$1,500
Ice Capades Doll	$1,800 up
Lavender Skirt with Striped Shirt, #2114, 1957	$750
Lavender Tulle Ball Gown, 1961	$1,800 up
Mauve Taffeta Torso Gown with Multi-Colored Bow, #2100, 1955	$1,000
Melanie *(Gone with the Wind)*	$1,500 up
Navy Taffeta Cocktail Dress with Jacket, #2084, 1955	$875
Navy Taffeta Cocktail Dress with White Organdy Cape, #2141, 1957	$875
Organdy Party Dress with Rosebuds and Hat, #2035, 1956	$1,150
Pink Camellia Gown, #2283, 1958	$1,250
Pink Dotted Nylon Gown, #2160, 1957	$1,000
Polished Cotton Dress with Lace Trim, #2130, 1957	$700
Purple Velvet Torso Gown, #2174, 1957	$1,000
Queen, white or gold brocade	$1,200
Red Cotton Dress with Striped Blouse, #2083, 1955	$750
Red Dotted Organdy Dress and Hat, #2019, 1956	$750
Red Taffeta Gown with Tulle Stole, #2285, 1958	$1,100
Renoir Cissy	$1,500
Satin Ball Gown with Fur Stole, #2041, 1956	$1,050
Scarlett Cissy	$1,500 up
Taffeta Cocktail Dress with Pillbox Hat, #2012, 1956	$850
Taffeta Torso Gown, red, shell pink, or rose, #2036, 1956	$1,100
Tulle Ankle Length Dress, blue or pink, #2025, 1956	$1,050
Tulle Gown with Floral Appliques, #2282, 1958	$1,200
Velvet Sheath Dress, #2231, 1958	$850
White Organdy Gown Trimmed in Lace and Red Roses, #2095, 1955	$1,200 up
Wool Chemise Dress, #2233, 1958	$750
Yachting Slacks Set, #2205, 1958	$800
Yellow Floral Dress, #2120, 1957	$875
Accessory Set	$175
Ball Gown (organdy, satin, taffeta, tulle, or velvet)	$1,000 up
Coat and Hat Ensemble (flannel, faux fur, velvet or wool)	$600 up

Cocktail Dress Ensemble (satin, taffeta, velvet, organdy, or tulle, may have hat, stole or jacket)	$950 up
Day Dress Ensemble (dotted swiss, moiré, cotton, taffeta, nylon, or organdy, may have hat)	$650 up
Lingerie (corsets, bra and panty sets, chemise, or slip)	$500 up
Nightgown, Robe, Peignoir Sets	$400 up
Pant Sets	$775 up
Satin Opera Coat, full length	$600 up
Skirt Sets	$650 up
Suits	$650 up
Swimsuits and Cabana Sets	$550 up
Cissy Takes a Trip, trunk and wardrobe set, F.A.O. Schwarz exclusive, 1956- 1957	$1,800 up
Royal Trunk Trousseau, F.A.O. Schwarz exclusive, 1960	$1,800 up
Yardley Ads, 1956-1957	$15-$150
Paper Doll Set by Peck Aubry, 1994	$25
Modern Cissy	
Enchanted Evening Portrait, 1991-1992	$300
Lilac Fairie Ballerina, 1993-1994	$300
Coral and Leopard travel ensemble, LE of 2500 dolls, 1996	$300
Ebony and Ivory Houndstooth suit, African American, LE unknown, 1996	$625
Caucasian, LE of 2500 dolls, 1996	$400
Café Rose and Ivory cocktail dress, African American, LE unknown, 1996	$600
Caucasian, LE of 2500 dolls, 1996	$400
Aquamarine evening column and coat, LE of 2500 dolls, 1996	$300
Onyx Velvet Lace gala gown and coat, LE of 2500 dolls, 1996	$375
Pearl Embroidered Lace bridal gown, LE of 2500 dolls, 1996	$550
Red Sequin gown, LE of 2500 dolls, 1996	$375
Daisy Resort ensemble, LE of 2500 dolls, 1997	$350
Tea Rose Cocktail ensemble, also available as African American, LE of 2500 dolls, 1997	$275
Gardenia Gala Ball Gown, LE of 2500 dolls, 1997	$275
Peony and Butterfly wedding gown, LE of 2500 dolls, 1997	$375
Calla Lily Evening column and bolero, LE of 2500 dolls, 1997	$450

Madame Butterfly, 1997	$350
Secret Armoire trunk set, 1997-1998	$900
Paris ensemble, LE of 1500 dolls, 1998	$550
Barcelona ensemble, also available as African American, LE of 1500 dolls, 1998	$350
Milan ensemble, LE of 1500 dolls, 1998	$400
Venice ensemble, LE of 1500 dolls, 1998	$400
Budapest ensemble, LE of 1500 dolls, 1998	$575
Ultimate Angel, 1998-1999	$400
Jessica McClintock ensemble, LE of 600 dolls, 1999	$350
Fernando Sanchez ensemble, LE of 600 dolls, 1999	$350
Josie Natori ensemble, LE of 600 dolls, 1999	$350
Anna Sui ensemble, LE of 600 dolls, 1999	$350
Linda Allard for Ellen Tracy ensemble, LE of 500 dolls, 1999	$350
Dana Buchman ensemble, LE of 600 dolls, 1999	$350
James Purcell ensemble, LE of 600 dolls, 1999	$350
Badgley Mischka ensemble, LE of 600 dolls, 1999	$350
Carolina Herrera ensemble, LE of 300 dolls, 1999	$350
Mark Bouwer ensemble, LE of 500 dolls, 1999	$350
Madame Alexander Celebrates American Design, LE of 1500 dolls, 1999	$325
Holiday Cissy, LE of 700 dolls, 1999	$300
Cairo Cissy, 2000	$400
Hollywood Cissy, also available as African American, 2000	$450
New York Cissy, 2000	$350
Rome Cissy, 2000	$400
Shanghai Cissy, 2000	$300
Vienna Cissy, 2000	$400
Romantic Dreams Cissy, 2000	$350
Atlanta Stroll Scarlett, 2000	$500
Yardley Cissy, 1st doll in series wearing steel blue dress, LE of 750, 2000	$450
Peacock Rose Cissy, LE of 600, 2000	$1,000
Society Stroll Cissy, LE of 500 dolls, 2001	$350
Society Stroll Cissy, African American, LE of 250, 2001	$350
Royal Reception Cissy, LE of 500 dolls, 2001	$350

Black and White Ball Cissy, LE of 500 dolls, 2001	$350
Cissy Haute Couture, LE of 500 dolls, 2001	$350
On the Avenue Yardley Cissy, green suit, 2nd doll in the Yardley series, LE of 500 dolls, 2001	$400
Promise of Spring Cissy, LE of 500 dolls, 2001	$500
Madame du Pompadour Cissy, LE of 100, 2001	$1,700
Manhattan Gothic Cissy, LE of 100, 2001	$1,200
Prima Donna Cissy, LE of 100, 2001	$1,200
Peachtree Promenade Scarlett, LE of 500, 2001	$500
Morning Ritual Yardley Cissy, 3rd in the Yardley series, LE of 500 dolls, 2001	$250
Alluring Amethyst Cissy, Caucasian, LE of 350, 2001	$400
America the Beautiful Cissy, 2001	$450
Maimey Cissy, LE of 350, 2002	$500
Bluebird Cissy, LE of 350, 2002	$500
Bluebird Cissy, African American, LE of 150, 2002	$500
Renaissance Garden Cissy, LE of 350, 2002	$500
Taffeta Romance Cissy, LE of 350, 2002	$550
Dance the Night Away Cissy, LE of 350, 2002	$450
Baby Doe Cissy, LE of 200, 2002	$650
Equestrian Cissy, LE of 200, 2002	$500
Pompadour Spring Cissy, LE of 200, 2002	$800
Queen Elizabeth Recessional, LE of 250, 2002	$950
Matron of the Mansion Scarlett, LE of 250, 2002	$550
Sitting Pretty Yardley Cissy, Diamond Dealer Doll, 4th in the Yardley Series, LE of 500, 2002	$500
80th Anniversary Cissy, LE of 200, 2002	$550
A Day in the Life of Cissy Trunk Set, LE of 500, wardrobe in steamer trunk, 2001	$450
Cissy's European Holiday Trunk Set, LE of 350, wardrobe in steamer trunk, 2002	$550
Cissy Shoe Accessory Package #1, 6 pairs of shoes in a hat box, 2000-2002	$60
Cissy Shoe Package, 6 pairs of shoes, 2001-2002	$70
Cissy Hatbox, includes, shoes, handbag, stockings, gloves, hat and earrings, 2001	$70

Exclusive Cissy	
Cissy by Scassi, F.A.O. Schwarz exclusive, 1990	$300
Gardenia Gala, blonde hair, MADC, 1997	$350
Miss St. John Cissy, Neiman-Marcus, 1998	$450
Arnold Scassi ensemble, Danbury Mint, 1999	$450
Fortune Teller, Collector's United, 1999	$750
Lilly Pulitzer ensemble, MADC, 1999	$900
Cissy Gala, MADC, 2000	$300
Cissy Gala Centerpiece, MADC, 2000	$525
Homecoming Queen Cissy, CU Greenville, African American, 2000	$400
Homecoming Queen Cissy, CU Greenville, Caucasian, 2000	$275
Irish Cissy, CU Nashville, 2000	$550
Alluring Amethyst, African American, Collector's United, 2001	$500
Blue Danube, African American, CU Nashville, 2001	$550
Blue Danube, Caucasian, CU Nashville, 2001	$325
Cissy Evening at the Pops, MADC Convention, 2001	$285
Cissy Diva, MADC Convention, 2001	$600
140th Anniversary Cissy Doll, FAO Schwarz, 2001	$600
On the Avenue Yardley Cissy, UFDC Convention, 2001	$500
Scarlett Cissy, Collector's United, 2001	$350
Coca Cola Cissy, Collector's United, 2002	$350
June Bride, MADC Convention, 2002	$300
June Bridesmaid, MADC Convention, 2002	$525
Sketchbook Cissy, MADC Convention, 2002	$525
Accessory Pak, exclusive for MADC Cissy Breakfast, 1999	$45
Cissy June Bride Lingerie set, MADC Convention Cissy event, 2002	$45

About the Authors

Benita Cohen Schwartz

Benita Cohen Schwartz is considered to be an authority on Madame Alexander dolls. For over twenty years she has collected and documented literally thousands of the creations from the Alexander Doll Company.

Benita has also been an active member of The Madame Alexander Doll Club and served on the Board of Directors as well as hosting numerous successful events for its members.

In 1994, Schwartz established F&M Productions, which sponsors quality doll shows up and down the East Coast.

Her many accomplishments also include being the host of the first five Gene® doll conventions to honor the popular fashion doll created by Mel Odom and the Ashton-Drake Galleries™. In addition, her articles on collectible dolls have appeared in *Doll Show Magazine, Doll Reader, Fashion Doll Scene* and on various web sites.

In addition to a love of Madame Alexander dolls, Benita has an extensive collection of Dawn® dolls, which was one of her favorite toys as a child. She is the author of *Dawn® Dolls Official Encyclopedia & Price Guide* (Hobby House Press, Inc. 2001).

Besides her career and accomplishments in the doll world, Benita is the mother of Farin, age 11, who while sharing her mother's love of dolls has ambitions of being a future ice skating champion. Benita is also the past president of the PTO at Farin's school.

A life long native of New Jersey, this Fairlawn-based author enjoys sharing her vast knowledge of 20th century dolls. The reader of this book will certainly agree that her astute observations make collecting easier and lots more fun!

A. Glenn Mandeville

A. Glenn Mandeville is certainly no stranger to Madame Alexander dolls. A native of central New Jersey, Glenn has a life-long interest in dolls and doll collecting.

"I used to stand in front of the glass cabinets at John Wanamaker's during the holidays and look at the beautiful Cissy dolls and other Alexander dolls," says Glenn. "Fortunately, my childhood playmate came from a family that indulged her every whim and we spent many fond hours playing with her dolls, as she did with my trains."

In the mid-1980s, Glenn was approached by Hobby House Press, Inc. to write magazine articles. This resulted in more articles for other magazines and finally the big step to books.

A former Spanish and French teacher, Mandeville spent his summers at the flea markets and eventually starting buying and selling dolls, gradually turning a small outdoor business into a thriving full time career of buying and selling the finest in collectible dolls. He recently joined the internet world with the launch of his website, www.aglennmandeville.com.

Glenn has also held numerous positions in United Federation of Doll Clubs, Inc. including Regional Director and Chairman of Judges/Modern. He has also served as past president of the Madame Alexander Doll Club.

Mandeville has been a frequent guest on radio and television with appearances on the RKO Radio Network, ABCs *Regis and Kathie Lee*, CNBC's Smart Money, and NBCs *Eddie Huggins*. To date he has evaluated and judged literally thousands of dolls and is considered an expert in dolls of the 20th century.

My goal was to preserve and document the playthings of the past and it is a goal that many collectors share. In this book, collectors will find many new tidbits of knowledge!

Index